KU-362-434

Contents

List of Illustrations

Past-into-Present Series

NURSING

Monica Baly

B.T.BATSFORD LTD
London

First published 1977
© Monica Baly 1977

ISBN 0 7134 2222 X

Printed in Great Britain by
The Anchor Press Ltd, Tiptree, Essex
for the Publishers B.T. Batsford Ltd,
4 Fitzhardinge Street, London W1H 0AH

Frontispiece (overleaf)
Nurse with child, from the frieze of The Seven Works of Mercy, in glazed and coloured relief in terra cotta, by Filippo Paladini (Ospedale del Ceppo, Italy, 15th century)

CLASS ✓ WY A00
11 508779
BAL

EAST CUMBRIA
EDUCATION CENTRE
LIBRARY

Acknowledgment

The Author and Publishers would like to thank the following for their kind permission to reproduce copyright illustrations: British Leyland Motor Corporation Ltd for fig 57; the Central Office of Information for figs 58, 60-3 (Crown copyright reserved); Greater London Council for fig 39; the Imperial War Museum for figs 43-6; A F Kersting for fig 10; the London Hospital for fig 35; the Mansell Collection for the frontispiece, figs 2, 3, 9, 13, 14, 19, 22, 24, 30, 33-4, 36; Mary Evans Picture Library for figs 5, 11, 18, 20-1, 23, 25-6, 37-8; the National Army Museum for figs 40, 52; the National Portrait Gallery for figs 27-8, 31; *Nursing Times* for figs 42, 50, 53-4; Radio Times Hulton Picture Library for figs 4, 6, 7, 12, 16, 17, 29, 32, 49, 51, 55-6; the Royal College of Nursing for figs 47-8, 64-5; the Welsh School of Medicine for fig 59. The other pictures appearing in the book are the property of the Publishers.

Introduction

Traditionally, nurses were people who did tasks for those too old or too young, too sick or too frail to do them for themselves. Often these tasks were done within the family. Sometimes groups of people with a high sense of charity, religion or vocation gave care to those without family or means. Others were motivated by money; waiting on the sick was merely a variation of waiting on those who were well. Although the standard of care given by these nurses varied, it had one thing in common: it was unscientific.

In tracing the development of nursing before the nineteenth century it is difficult to decide what was nursing and what was not. Were the early deaconesses nurses any more than the sick attendants in the eighteenth century? Wise women and witches with their faith cures and concoctions — were they nurses? Another problem is that those who gave service were often poor and illiterate and the poor do not leave records; there are no substantial accounts of nursing written by nurses until the time of Miss Nightingale (1820—1910). Moreover, for much of history illness has been accepted as inevitable and the will of God; there was, therefore, little point in intervention and the inevitable was hardly worthy of chronicle.

Then came the scientific revolution. Men like Louis Pasteur (1822—95) and Robert Koch (1843—1910) identified the bacteria that caused disease; Joseph Lister (1827—1912) introduced antiseptic surgery and Sir James Simpson (1811—70) anaesthetics. By 1900, medicine could successfully prevent, cure and relieve illness. Coinciding with this revolution was a new system of training; nurses became educated and skilled, capable of helping doctors with their new scientific medicine. The new image was of a *hospital* nurse associated with doctors and the curing of disease.

However, this is just one side of a nurse's work. The unique contribution of nursing is to give *care*. If nursing is a profession in its own right then we must move away from this limited vision of a hospital nurse as the adjunct to doctors and cure. Today nurses are helping to plan medical services, prevent illness and rehabilitate the handicapped and, when the time comes, they help their patients to a peaceful death. Attitudes, knowledge and health problems may have changed over the years, but the task of the nurse remains the same: to prevent and relieve suffering and give care to those who need it.

1
Early Nursing

Attitudes to Care

Although there have always been people who for pity's sake have given care to the sick and suffering, nursing as we know it is a comparatively recent development.

For most of history, man's numbers have been kept down by famine. As he scratched a living from the soil, many of the ills from which he suffered — rickets, scurvy and rheumatism — were caused by lack of proper food and shelter. What was needed was better farming and distribution of food, not doctors and nurses.

Apart from the fact that the first needs were for a better standard of living, organized care for those who were ill was for many years inhibited by the contradictory attitudes of the Church. The early Church believed that suffering was the will of God and as such was the passport to eternal life. Did not the Bible tell them that Lazarus, the poor man whose sores were licked by dogs, went to heaven, while the rich man, Dives, went to hell? If suffering was the will of God then to interfere with the course of illness would be to defy God.

At the same time, mixed with Christian attitudes were deeper, primitive beliefs. From earliest times men believed that good and evil came from supernatural sources and that bad fortune was the result of a god's displeasure. This might be due to the failure to make a sacrifice, perform a ritual, or observe a taboo. In order to regain favour with the god, these omissions had to be rectified. In antiquity people often used priests, priestesses and magicians to act as intermediaries. In primitive societies in the Christian era there was a tendency to favour witches and sorcerers, and in the next chapter we shall see how this belief had an upsurge in the sixteenth century with disastrous effect.

Some early societies believed that the displeasure of the god was the result of sin and this idea dominates much of the Old Testament. St Augustine of Hippo (AD 345—430) took this theory to its ultimate conclusion when he wrote: 'All diseases are to be ascribed to demons.'

1 This picture, painted by Henner in the mid-nineteenth century when there was a revival of interest in the early Church, is an idealized portrayal of Fabiola. It is sometimes used to remind nurses of their early Christian heritage.

Early Christian Nursing

Although the early Church was confused as to whether diseases were due to demons or the will of God, a clear duty had been laid on the first disciples to comfort and relieve the sick. To help with this mission in the first centuries after Christ, the Church organized women, called deaconesses, to visit the sick and needy. St Paul, in his epistle to the Romans, speaks of Phoebe, a fellow Christian, 'who holds office in the congregation at Cenchrea and who has been the good friend to many'. These deaconesses inspired many women converts to take up nursing the sick. Perhaps best known is Fabiola because of her romantic picture by J J Henner (1829–1905). Fabiola was a wealthy Roman lady who became the friend of St Jerome (died 420). After two unhappy marriages while still young, she gave up wealth and position to devote her life to the sick. St Jerome says of her, 'How often did she carry the sick on her shoulders. How often did she wash the putrid matter from wounds another could not bear to look on. With her own hands she prepared their food, and moistened with water the parched lips of the dying'. By the time she died in AD 399 Fabiola had made nursing the sick and poor fashionable in Roman society. But this was not to last. After the recognition of Christianity in AD 335, Christians began to dislike and fear the material world of Rome, and groups of devout men and women moved away to live in isolation. As the monasteries were established, the early Christian tradition of nursing in the community was lost. Hereafter, as we shall see, there was a tendency for the patients to go to the nurses rather than the other way round.

Although the early monasteries withdrew from the world the monks remained the custodians of ancient learning and, as they translated the works of the Greek physicians like Hippocrates and Aristotle, they put their knowledge into practice – not for the benefit of ordinary people, but for their sick brethren.

Cassiodorius, a friend of St Benedict, writing in AD 575 exhorts the monks:

> To serve with honest study to aid the sick as becomes the knowledge of medicine. Learn the nature of herbs and how to combine the various kinds. If you cannot read Greek read a translation of Hippocrates, Galen and Aurelius Caelius.

Although the monastic infirmaries were intended for the care of ill monks, some orders – particularly St Augustine and St Benedict – organized brotherhoods and sisterhoods to give care to the sick who lived near by. Gradually care was extended to pilgrims, and later monasteries began to provide buildings for the different categories of the needy. The building for the sick was called a *nosokomeion*. Here the patients were washed and fed, probably purged and bled, and undoubtedly exhorted to prepare for eternal life.

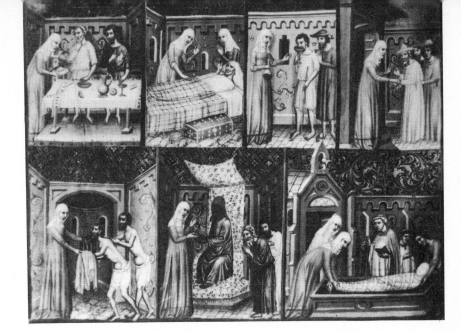

2 A 'strip cartoon' of early hospital life. Travellers admitted through the top door are fed and cared for by the nuns in sickness and in health. In the last picture, (bottom right) a pilgrim who has died is being prepared for his last earthly journey.

Health in Medieval England

After the collapse of the Roman Empire in the fifth century AD the population of Europe declined, but the torch of scholarship was kept alight by the monasteries. Many orders were firmly established in England by the time the Normans conquered the country in 1066. At this time, life for most of the one and a half million people in England was harsh. The death rate was high and half the children who were born died in early infancy. As the philosopher Thomas Hobbes (1588–1679) wrote later, there was 'continual fear and danger of violent death; and the life of man solitary, poor, nasty, brutish and short'.

3 The Norman Conquest, part of the Bayeux tapestry. Notice the domestic scenes on the bottom panel: the meat is being cooked on a spit and skewered on arrows and the serfs' houses have no windows.

The feudal system of land holding meant that most people were bound to a lord and his demesne and had few rights. Indeed, when the *Domesday Book* was compiled in 1086 there were still 25,000 people classed as 'slaves'. Most people were serfs, eking out a mean existence from strips of land in the manorial fields and from grazing rights on common land. Agriculture was uncertain: in a wet summer, or drought, crops would fail and the small supply of meat might well be infected by the 'murrain' — a medieval 'foot and mouth' disease.

Not only was food short, shelter was primitive. We know from the embroidered details on the Bayeux Tapestry that villagers lived in simple, single- or double-chamber 'cruck' dwellings that gave little light or ventilation and whose floor was simply the earth covered with rushes. As well as being undernourished, the serf was often the victim of rheumatism and skeletons show that arthritis and crippling were common.

At the beginning of the Norman period, pilgrimages and the Crusades to the Holy Land increased travel to and from the Mediterranean and new diseases began to appear in England. During the twelfth century there was an upsurge of leprosy and at one time there were 20,000 leper houses in Christendom. It is unlikely that all the unfortunates in these houses had true leprosy, for diagnosis was questionable and the term covered a variety of skin conditions. These 'lazars' as they were called were officially 'declared dead' and cast out of the town. Without a family and with no hope of employment, shunned and thought 'unclean', they were forced to roam the countryside begging for alms. However, although this treatment was cruel and inhumane, it was, curiously enough, an important step in medical history. For reasons that were quite unscientific, medieval doctors took over the biblical ritual of making lepers 'outcasts'. From this developed the idea that certain groups of patients, especially those with skin eruptions, should not be nursed with others and that such nursing was dangerous. Rashes are often a sign that the patient has an infectious fever, so sometimes the doctors did the right thing for the wrong reason. The lazar hospitals outside the towns were the forerunners of our isolation hospitals.

Another disease considered dangerous to nurse was typhus. Long associated with war and famine, it now spread over Europe and attacked the poor in the growing, insanitary towns. At the same time increased travel brought smallpox and measles to northern Europe. Known as 'the pox and mesles' they were often confused; at first the attacks were mild, but as they took hold of the population they became more deadly and at times, in the sixteenth century and later, smallpox was the 'Captain of Killers'. But the greatest scourge of medieval man was, undoubtedly, bubonic plague. Death from the plague was often swift and violent. The great epidemic of 1348, afterwards known as the Black Death, left a trail of devastation and disaster and reduced the population of Europe by about one-third.

4 Edward I (1239-1307) giving a 'touch piece' to a leper. The superstition that certain skin diseases could be cured by the king's touch persisted until the eighteenth century.

Village Nursing

In the early Middle Ages, because of the attitude of the Church and the hazards of life, there was little point in providing organized care for the sick. Most people accepted suffering as the will of God or looked for help in their village. Here there were numerous quacks and imposters, 'men and women who practised physyk to the grete harm and slaughter of many men'. The chronicles tell of Alice Shevyngton, a maidservant earning 16 shillings a year, who left her master 'and took to curing people with sore eyes'. Afflictions of the eyes were common and no doubt Alice found ophthalmic nursing more rewarding than being a servant.

5 Attending a mother in child-birth. This is a wealthy family because there are three attendants looking after the lying-in mother. The nurse is holding the new born baby in front of the fire before putting it in swaddling clothes.

As well as quacks and wise women, most villages had a midwife who assisted in childbirth and, unfortunately, much else besides, so passing on infections to mothers and babies. Other people looked to witches for help. There was a widespread belief that evil could be transferred with the aid of spells and charms. Some were simple, others were involved incantations and prescriptions and were apt to imply magic transference; for example, the man with an impediment in his speech was given a concoction made from the tongue of a hound. The people who provided such spells and charms carried on a profitable trade until the later Middle Ages when the Church, having decided that witches were in league with the devil, ordered them to be burnt. However, with its reliance on holy relics and insistence on miraculous cures, the Church was hardly more scientific. Even the new surgeon barbers of the twelfth century refused to operate unless the stars were favourable. The study of astrology was more important than the study of anatomy.

Monastic Hospitals

In the twelfth century Europe was an open society without frontiers and barriers, with the Church as the unifying intellectual force. As the members of the various religious houses moved across Christendom they took new ideas with them. When in AD 1198 Pope Innocent III built the San Spirito hospital for the poor in Rome, this example and the growing needs of the population led to further endowments in other countries. Hospices, like the Hotels Dieu that had been set up earlier for pilgrims along their main routes, were now reestablished as hospitals. In London the monk Rahere founded St Bartholomew's on the northern road into the city, and later Bishop Peter de Roches rebuilt the hospice at Southwark, on the southern route, and dedicated it to St Thomas the Martyr.

The picture on this page of the Hotel Dieu in Paris, although drawn in the sixteenth century, gives us some idea what the wards were like in these hospitals. Here the patients are nursed two in a bed and are attended by nuns of St Augustine. The patients seem very ill, indeed one is receiving the last sacrament, while two nuns sew a shroud. From the picture the ward seems well staffed, but no doubt in real life it was more crowded. The life of a nursing nun was hard: work started on the ward at 5 am and went on until 7 pm. The nuns not only cared for the patients and gave the treatments, they also did the cooking and cleaning and enduring their greatest trial — washing the hospital linen standing in the icy waters of the River Seine. There was no question of what was a 'non-nursing' duty; all tasks were to the glory of God.

Military Nursing

In the eleventh century a hospice was built in Jerusalem to serve the pilgrims to the Holy Sepulchre. The hospice was run by a group calling themselves the Order of St John, and during the first Crusades the order cared for a number of knights, many of whom made generous donations. As the order became wealthy, they reconstituted themselves as military monks under the rule of St Augustine. Their uniform was a black habit surmounted with a white, eight-pointed cross, which is still used by the St John's Ambulance Brigade.

Another famous group of hospitallers was the Knights Templars but they were more concerned with the protection of travellers than the care of the sick. In England we have cause to remember the Templars because, when they were expelled from the Holy Land in 1187, they brought the hospice of Bethlehem to Bishopsgate in London; later it became a hospital for the insane, and the corruption of the word 'Bethlehem' has survived in our language as 'Bedlam'.

6 Triptych showing the Hotel Dieu in Paris about 1500. Notice there are two patients to a bed, with the comparatively well on the right separated from the very ill on the left. The left is what we would call today a 'terminal care' unit.

The hospital of Bethlehem, which has now moved out of London to Beckenham in Kent, is still one of our most famous hospitals for the mentally sick.

The Knights of St John built a number of hospitals across Europe. Fine examples remain in Rhodes and Malta and from these we can envisage the high standard of care given. If the records at Rhodes are correct then the ratio of nurses to patients, particularly at night, was better than in a modern hospital. The Crusader hospitals were important because they were concerned with saving the valuable lives of the Crusaders: unlike the monasteries who were happy to commit the poor to the will of God, the brotherhood of St John was always seeking ways of curing the knights and getting them back into the fighting force. This is why we get the paradox that the greatest advances in medicine and the care of the sick are often made in war. Because they were a wealthy, international organization straddled across Europe, the hospitallers were able to exchange ideas about treatment and drugs in many countries. One of the more important sources of ideas was Islam. The Arabs, having taken over and absorbed the libraries of the Greek physicians, added their own independent contributions in chemistry, drugs, mathematics and hospital organization. This was the hey-day of Arab medicine and their ideas spread into Europe via the University of Salerno in Italy, where fresh notions of medicine were to form the basis of reformed medical training in the universities.

Other Nursing Orders
In the Middle Ages, the Church put a new emphasis on the importance of charity and inspired nobly born women to found hospitals and care for the poor and the sick. As in the time of Fabiola in the fourth century, nursing became fashionable. However, do not forget that the Church insisted that the way to cure was through prayer and fasting, calling on the help of the saints and a belief in miracles, and the new, aristocratic nurses relied just as much on divine help as the nuns. Margaret of Scotland not only built hospitals but she also nursed the sick of Edinburgh with her own hands. Her daughter, who married Henry I (1100), and who was known as Queen Maud or sometimes Matilda, carried on the nursing tradition founding hospitals and nursing the lepers of London. Another queen who was associated with the endowment of hospitals in the twelfth century was Matilda, wife of King Stephen (1135–54).

At the same time, the death of many Crusaders increased the number of women without husbands and some of these entered convents. Others found opportunity for service with the friars and set up nursing orders outside the cloisters. In England the friars gave religion a new spirit and new methods; they created a religious revival rather like the Wesleyans and the Salvation Army later. The brothers moved around the countryside preaching to the poor while the 'little sisters' gave service to the sick from the various houses in which they established themselves. The development of medicine in England at this time owes much to the followers of St Francis, but most of the hospitals and schools

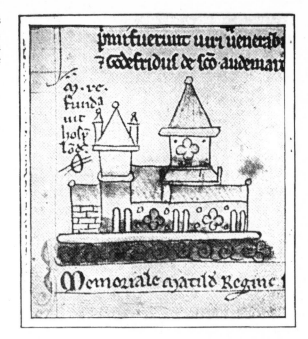

7 The Leper Hospital of St Giles in the fields of Holborn, London. The hospital was founded by Queen Maud at the beginning of the twelfth century.

they founded were taken over during the dissolution of the monasteries (1536–39). Place names still sometimes indicate where the friars worked, for example there is a street in Aldgate, London, called 'Minories' where the little sisters of St Francis — the 'minoresses' — had their hospital.

The uncloistered nursing brothers and sisters were important because they showed that nursing and medicine — and the two were often inseparable — were not the prerogative of wealthy monasteries, and good works could be performed without people taking vows of chastity and obedience. This idea of a 'nursing order' outside the Church was revived by St Vincent de Paul (see page 22) in the seventeenth century and continued to attract nursing reformers until the end of the nineteenth century.

There was, however, antagonism between the established and the newer 'uncloistered' orders. The bishops grew anxious about the lack of conformity of the free orders who mingled with the corrupt world and were not under the control of the Church. There were clashes between the Church and the friars, and disputes between the Franciscans and the Dominicans paved the way for the Reformation. As the tensions mounted the brothers and sisters, whose only desire was to do good in the world, found themselves denounced as 'heretics' and in England they lost their property with the dissolution of the monasteries.

The light of charity that had burned, if somewhat intermittently, during the Middle Ages was gradually extinguished as controversy about the doctrine of the Church and the ideas of the Reformation raged round Europe. As the fires burned to save men's souls from heresy, there was little time to think about ways of saving sick bodies.

2

The End of the Age of Faith

Social Change, 1300–1600

Until about 1350, the Church was mainly responsible for organized care of the sick. This care, as we have seen, was given by monks and nuns who had taken vows and, from the twelfth century, by 'uncloistered' nursing orders as well.

Now, in the second half of the fourteenth century, the whole monastic and feudal system showed signs of strain. The Black Death in 1348 caused a dramatic fall in the population and, as a result, landholding changed and labour became scarce. Labourers were now able to demand higher wages and there was less poverty. William Langland (c. 1332–1400), the chronicler, wrote:

> Hunger was no longer Master. Beggars refused bread made of beans and demanded milk loaves or fine wheaten bread and the best brown ale.... Day labourers turned up their noses at anything but fresh meat and fried or baked fish, served hot, lest they catch a chill on their stomachs.

8 Costume used by doctors visiting patients stricken by the plague. It is described as being made of leather, the eye-piece of glass and the long nose stuffed with perfumes. As the plague was carried by the rat flea it would have been better to have got rid of the rats.

During the plague nearly half the clergy had died and some religious houses had collapsed. But, in spite of the number of monks who died helping plague victims, there was a feeling that the Church had failed the people and its prayers had been unanswered. At the same time, groups like the Lollards, who followed the teachings of the scholar John Wycliffe, and men from the new universities began to attack the worldliness of the Church and urged its reform. When the Papacy turned a deaf ear more extreme reform movements developed, which attacked not only the worldliness of the Church but also its doctrine. By the sixteenth century there were two agressive Christian faiths — Protestant and Catholic — each determined to conquer the Christian world. As they became embroiled in deadly conflict, the attitudes of charity and compassion that had been fostered by the Church in the twelfth century passed into oblivion.

The Renaissance

The climate was now one of change. Voyages of exploration showed men that some traditional teaching was false, and inventions like Galileo's telescope opened up a more scientific approach to the nature of the universe. The universities of Europe produced men of a different outlook, there were new translations of old authors and a flowering of imaginative writing and poetry took place. However, there was little original thought about the nature of disease; there was no advance on the ideas of the Greek physicians until 1616, when William Harvey (1578–1657) discovered how the blood circulated. This continuing lack of knowledge about disease, together with the bigoted and fanatical attitudes engendered by religious strife, accounts for what has been described as the 'Dark Ages of Nursing'.

The Reformation and the Witch Craze

Against this background, the Reformation in England pursued its own peculiar course. Henry VIII was a good Catholic but his marriage problems and his need for money made him break with Rome. Henry's plan was to dissolve the monasteries and set up a reorganized system with himself as head of Church and State, but for various reasons the plan never fully matured and little attempt was made to replace the nursing services given by the monks and nuns. In fact, there was little demand for this. In the first place, it is unlikely that many people were actually benefiting from the monastic hospitals and there is evidence that the infirmaries were misused. Secondly, nursing orders smacked of the Pope and of Rome and, as the tide turned against Catholicism, they became increasingly unpopular. Thirdly, the attitude towards sickness was still that it was sent from God and was the result of sin. Thomas Cranmer's new prayer book shows little departure from this attitude. The Book of Common Prayer still contains this gem:

For Deliverance from Plague and other common Sickness
O Lord who has wounded us for our sins, and consumed us for our transgres-

sions, by thy late heavy and dreadful visitation; and now, in the midst of judgement remembering mercy, has redeemed our souls from the jaws of death.

There is no doubt that the Church continued to do its best to ensure that men regarded their afflictions as the result of sin and their recovery as God's mercy.

However, there was also a more sinister reason why caring for the sick ceased to be an honourable calling. As the Protestants and Catholics became locked in religious wars all over Europe, the 'Witch Craze' revived. This mania was essentially derived from the 'devil doctrine' established by the Church in the Middle Ages and used to root out heretics. Now, as passions became inflamed, both Catholics and Protestants saw the work of the devil in their adversaries. As the terrible cult of witch hunting and witchcraft spread, so it became a form of mass hysteria. The torture and the witch trials multiplied, and the denunciations began to include not only mentally disturbed old women, but also educated men and women and even young children. Accusations of witchcraft were a convenient way of getting rid of political enemies or unwanted members of your family. Between 1623 and 1631 the Prince-Bishop of Wurzburg in Germany burned 900 people, including his own nephew and a number of young children. In England, during the Civil War (1642–9), the famous witch hunter Matthew Hopkins was responsible for hanging 60 people in one year in Essex alone. Later, Matthew Hopkins himself was accused of sorcery. Superstition had it that witches always floated in water, so the test of witchcraft was to throw the suspect in the river: those who floated were in league with the devil, while those who sank were innocent. Matthew floated and was hanged.

The connection between witchcraft and healing is not hard to find. 'Black Magic' calls on a diabolical agency to inflict harm on someone. 'White Magic' calls on a benevolent spirit to do good and often, with the aid of magic herbs and charms, takes the form of treating illness. Here there was an obvious connection with the teaching of the Church, which had insisted that healing must be through supernatural intervention. Now, all healing was seen as connected with the supernatural and as the hunt for witches and sorcerers grew, people began to see magic, both black and white, everywhere. Thus few women dared to give treatment to the sick outside their homes, for fear of being denounced as a witch.

New Social Problems

Poverty had always been a problem, but until the sixteenth century it had mostly been confined within the parish and dealt with there. Now, discharged monastery servants, disbanded soldiers and labourers dispossessed by the new enclosures started to roam the countryside and become vagabonds. The sturdy beggar was the curse of Tudor times. 'Hark, hark, the dogs do bark the beggars are coming to town' is an old nursery rhyme that reminds us that Tudor mothers lived in fear of the bands of beggars who descended on the towns taking the law into their own hands.

9 The beggars are coming to town. The Tudors had a big unemployment problem which they tried to solve by the Poor Laws, but these had the effect of confining vagrants to their own parishes and prevented mobility of labour.

In 1536, the unsupported poor were made the responsibility of their own parish by law. Justices of the Peace were ordered to levy a weekly charge on all inhabitants, to be collected as a 'Poor Rate', and to appoint overseers of the poor. The problem was difficult because, as those who prepared the Acts recognized, there were many different causes of poverty. William Marshall, in a draft of the Poor Law Act of 1536, lists seven main causes of poverty, one of which was:

There be divers old, sick, lame, feeble and impotent persons not able to labour for their living but are driven of necessity to procure alms and charity of the people. And his highness [Henry VIII] has perfect knowledge that some of them have fallen into such poverty only of the visitation of God through sickness and other casualties.

The difficulty was to deal kindly with the sick and the old while getting tough with those who, Marshall says, 'lacked good oversight in their youth and never knew any other way of living except by begging'.

10 The Whitgift Almshouses, Croydon (1596-99). Whitgift became archbishop in 1583 and helped to frame the Poor Laws. At that time the archbishop's palace was at Croydon and Whitgift had these almshouses built as an example of the way parishes should separate the 'impotent poor' and put them into comfortable dwellings.

The Tudor Poor Laws dealt with the two main poverty groups, the unemployed and the sick. The Justices were responsible for seeing that the able-bodied beggars were rounded up, whipped and sent to Houses of Correction, where they were set to work. Those who belonged to another parish were sent back to their place of birth. The Poor Laws also laid down that parents and children must maintain their own relatives, and no doubt the Justices made sure they had as few 'impotent poor' on their hands as possible. For those who could not be cared for in their own homes, a register was kept and 'habitations' or Houses of Dwelling were provided, and Elizabethan and early Jacobean almshouses — now often architectural showpieces — can be seen to this day, for example, the Whitgift Almshouses, Croydon.

The Royal Hospitals
After the dissolution of the monasteries in the 1530s, there were requests by the citizens of London that some of the property and money confiscated be used to deal with the main social evils of the day. In the founding or refounding

of hospitals, however, the purpose was often changed. Instead of being places for the care of the sick, they now became refuges for the flotsam and jetsam of society that escaped the net of the Poor Laws.

The five 'Royal' hospitals endowed by Henry VIII and Edward VI were St Bartholomew's, St Thomas's, Bethlehem, Bridewell and Christ's Hospital. St Bartholomew's was reopened as a hospital because the worthy citizens of Smithfield disliked the smell of the sick lying about in the streets. St Thomas's was rededicated to St Thomas the Apostle — Becket the Martyr having gone out of fashion — and continued to deal with the sick of south London. The Bethlehem Hospital in Bishopsgate, the original hospice of St Mary of the Templars, was refounded and continued to give service to 'persons fallen out of their wits'. Bedlam must have been known to William Shakespeare for he makes Edgar, in *King Lear*, disguise himself as 'a poor Tom o' Bedlam'. These poor Toms were ex-patients from Bethlehem who were allowed to beg without being picked up under the vagrancy laws. Being in Bedlam had its advantages.

Bridewell Hospital was built on the estates at St Bride's Well, belonging to the Knights Hospitallers. When Henry VIII acquired the property he turned it into a palace; twenty-two years later in 1547, Edward VI gave it to the City of London and it became a House of Correction to deal with London's army of sturdy beggars. The term 'Bridewell' later came to mean a reformatory or prison. Christ's Hospital, which had belonged to the Franciscan Greyfriars, opened in 1555 for orphan children. Owing to the high rate of infection most of the children died, but the hospital continued and eventually became a famous public school, commonly known as the Bluecoat School.

11 Surgery in the seventeenth century. When medicine and surgery were so primitive and unscientific, it is no wonder that nursing was at a low ebb.

With the nuns expelled from their convents and aristocratic interest withdrawn, the character of nursing in these hospitals changed. The stage was set for the pattern that was to prevail in Protestant countries until the Nightingale reforms in the nineteenth century. The nuns were replaced by local women; at St Bartholomew's the sisters and saints gave way to the women of Smithfield, and the Mother Superior to a matron. Here, in 1549, the city authorities appointed the first matron to be responsible for the sisters and to see that they did their work properly. Their duties seem to have been mainly domestic and it is interesting to note that the nurses were warned 'not to remain with a sick person longer than necessary'. Since 15 out of every 20 patients in 1579 were said to be suffering from the Great Pox (later known as syphilis), which was then highly contagious, this may have been wise. However, it is an instruction that hardly denotes devotion.

The Vincentian Sisters of Charity

During the seventeenth century, while Europe was in the grip of the Thirty Years War (1618–48), Catholics of the Counter Reformation sought ways of overcoming the defects of the Catholic Church. One of these Catholics was St Vincent de Paul, who in 1611 accepted a poor parish in the south of France and undertook a series of preaching missions to the surrounding parishes bereft

12 St Vincent de Paul recovering foundlings left on the doorsteps in Paris. The Vincentian Sisters of Charity eventually became responsible for all the foundlings in Paris.

of spiritual guidance. One Sunday, during a sermon, St Vincent put forward the idea that the parishioners should form an 'Association of Charity' and take it in turns to visit the sick. Overwhelmed with offers, St Vincent drew up sets of rules for what might be considered a forerunner to a district nursing service. Instructions to the visitors included:

> The visitor should cook a substantial meal and take it to the patient; the patient should be washed and fed and made comfortable before the meal was served. If the patient was alone the visitor should stay longer and offer comfort and cheer.

St Vincent, it seems, had a better idea of the basic needs of patients than the authorities at St Bartholomew's.

As the Associations became known the idea spread, and when St Vincent left the area Madame Gondi, the wife of his patron, took over the organization of the Associations of Charity. However, St Vincent is better known for his work in the famous Hotel Dieu in Paris, where contemporary records tell of deterioration in the standard of the nursing. In Paris, as elsewhere, the sick were neglected, the hygiene was appalling and the food was poor. Several patients were nursed in one bed, with others lying on the floor, ready to scramble into a bed when a corpse was removed. Of the nuns a chronicler said: 'Some did nothing, others prayed and a few worked'.

After a plea for help from the Archbishop of Paris, St Vincent set about improving the standards of nursing care. The situation bristled with difficulties because, not unnaturally, the nuns resented outside interference. In order to get over the difficulty, St Vincent formed an Association of Charity of 100 ladies, including some of royal blood. The nuns could hardly refuse to be helped by

13 The 'Charity Ladies' helping the nursing brothers and sisters in the Hôpital de la Charité in Paris. It is doubtful if the ward was as well organized as it appears in this picure.

the nobility. Initially the experiment was a success, but St Vincent quickly realized that the ladies of the court were not really suitable for the job and were not likely to continue when the novelty of the scheme had worn off. So, with the help of a former penitent, Madame de Gras, he set about recruiting reliable Christian women who wanted to nurse in hospitals. Many applicants were from farming backgrounds, of humble origin, and if necessary Madame de Gras taught them to read and write. Madame de Gras's small house in Paris became the sisters' first home and 'school of nursing'. Here, the recruits were taught the elements of bedside care, how to use a lancet and tourniquet and how to apply poultices and bandages. The list of skills taught suggests that there were few doctors and the nurses often performed tasks that today we would consider the work of a doctor.

As time went by, the work of the new Sisters of Charity became well known and there was an increasing demand for their services. They worked in the terrible conditions of the Thirty Years War and in the army hospitals many of them died from infection and privation. However, within 20 years of their foundation they had 70 motherhouses in France and Poland and over 400 members. The order soon became world famous and a number of 'daughter' houses were set up in other parts of the Catholic world; by 1850, just before the outbreak of the Crimean War, there were 12,000 women working as Sisters of Charity.

The Vincentian Institute marked two notable innovations: firstly it was secular and secondly it was of the people. It had previously been thought that nursing sisters must take religious vows and that charity was the prerogative of wealth and the Church. The Vincentian ideal was a new concept of personal duty and it played an important part in the Catholic spiritual revival.

Two hundred years later, *The Times* war correspondent in the Crimea sent back despatches describing the complete lack of nursing care for the British army while the French had their wonderful Sisters of Charity. The next day there was a letter in the newspaper headed: 'Why has England no Sisters of Charity?'

This comparison was eventually the spur to nursing reform in England.

3
The Age of Reason

The Eighteenth-Century Outlook

By 1700 the religious and political upheavals that had so marred the previous century had subsided and a period of comparative peace began. In this atmosphere trade and overseas possessions increased. Instead of being a country that worked to feed itself first and used surplus labour for industry, England now became dependent on selling manufactured goods in order to pay for essential food imports. The old agricultural England was being replaced by a new industrial society.

Peace allowed people to travel more freely and it became customary for the upper classes to complete their education by going on the 'Grand Tour'. As we saw at the time of the Crusades, travel stimulates an exchange of ideas and encourages men to question old beliefs. In the years before the French Revolution of 1789, Europe was a ferment of new ideas. Men like Isaac Newton (1642–1727) had insisted that the universe was governed by natural laws of gravity and philosophers were beginning to suggest that there were natural reasons for such things as poverty, sickness and crime. Men thought that if they could find a reason for the disasters that overtook people, then soon they would find a remedy.

During this period of rapid expansion in trade and industry some people grew very rich. Many used their new wealth to make life more comfortable for themselves, but others — following new philosophies — wanted their money to be used to find reasons for, and to help relieve, social distress. This attitude was strengthened by new thinking in religion. Although the Church had become more tolerant after the religious wars of the seventeenth century, the Methodists urged a fresh approach. Together with groups like the Quakers, they strove to practise the teachings of the New Testament in place of the harsher doctrines of the Old. The new evangelists drew many converts and a spirit of charity and a new attitude to sickness were born.

The Gin Era

There was a dire need for a new outlook. In spite of the improved standards of living for the upper classes there was much grinding poverty below. Although there had been Town Improvement Acts, parts of the cities were squalid and insanitary. The law was chaotic and its enforcement haphazard. Those who fell foul of the law found themselves in the filthy prisons that were breeding grounds for typhus fever and vice. In the early 1700s, partly to satisfy the farming interest because distilling used corn, Parliament lightened the tax on gin. Because of this gin had tended to replace beer as the national drink of the poor. This led to an increase in drunkenness and crime, the horrors of which have been immortalized in *The Beggar's Opera* and in the famous panels of the engraver William Hogarth (1697—1764) of *Gin Lane* and *A Rake's Progress*.

14 This panel by William Hogarth was drawn to show the evils of gin drinking. On the left, people are pledging their goods to the pawnbroker in order to buy gin. Notice the suicide in the window on the right.

Because drunken mothers living in insanitary slums neglected their children, and because smallpox was particularly rife and virulent, the death rate rose. In 1740, 75 per cent of all children died before they were five years old, and between 1740 and 42 more babies were buried than were baptized. If this trend had continued the population would have fallen. But laws were eventually passed taxing gin and limiting its sale. English men and women went back to drinking the less lethal beer, which remained the national drink until it was ousted by the even more innocuous tea in the nineteenth century.

The Founding of Charity Hospitals

By the mid-eighteenth century there were two main types of institution for the sick. An Act of 1722 had allowed parishes to spend the poor rate on 'houses'

15 St Thomas's Hospital at its old site in Southwark during the eighteenth century. The hospital moved to its new position, opposite the Houses of Parliament, in the second half of the nineteenth century.

16 St Bartholomew's as it was rebuilt in 1775

for paupers. Little use was made of the Act because of the cost involved and most parishes preferred to give relief to people in their homes. However, in some places 'workhouses' housed people who were paupers because they were sick. The second type of institution was the charity hospital. At the beginning of the century there were already a few venerable hospitals, such as St Thomas's and St Bartholomew's; to these were added the new charity hospitals. The Westminster, Guy's, St George's, the London and the Middlesex were all opened between 1720 and 1745, and by the 1750s there were 30 similar charities in the provinces.

The move to found these hospitals came from the aristocracy and the wealthy who wished to do something to alleviate the evils of the day. Often these philanthropists founded hospitals to deal with a particular problem. For example, Mr Guy, a governor of St Thomas's, decided to set up a separate hospital for the incurables that St Thomas's was excluding. The Middlesex opened its doors 'to help the sick and lame of Soho'. The people who were admitted to these 'havens of care' were poor, but never destitute. Patients frequently had to guarantee their own funeral expenses and often pay a deposit for the use of sheets, towels and cutlery. Because of the fear of infection it soon became the practice to exclude those with skin and contagious diseases, and because of their susceptibility to infection no provision was made for children and lying-in mothers. Thus the real needs of the day were not met by these hospitals and the general improvement in health at the end of the century was due to a better supply of food and some improvements in sanitation rather than to advances in medicine and hospital care.

The Organization of Charity Hospitals

The charity hospitals were run by two groups of people: the paid and the unpaid. The governors, and often such people as the treasurers, gave their services free, and as time went by it became customary for the visiting doctors to be 'honorary'. Doctors gave their services partly from charitable motives, but largely because a hospital appointment added status and brought them recommendations for more private patients. The paid staff were few in number and were employed by the governors rather like servants in a large house.

17 The Middlesex Hospital opened in 1745 in two houses in Windmill Street, London. These soon proved too small and in 1754 the governors acquired land from Mr Berners and built the new imposing looking hospital.

Apart from the apothecary, who was responsible for the medicines, there was a steward, a chaplain and a matron. The matron was paid a salary — possibly about £40 a year — usually about half that paid to the chaplain. The low valuation of the matron may account for the fact that several earlier ones seem to have decamped with the patients' beer money. The matron was not a nurse. When the Middlesex Hospital opened in 1745, a doorkeeper was appointed and it was laid down that 'his wife be the matron and Sara Whittaker the nurse'. Sad to relate, the doorkeeper and his wife were soon dismissed for 'failing to acquaint the committee of several indecencies and irregularities'. All too soon they were followed by the apothecary, who was dismissed for 'actions vile and enormous'. The staff were not above corruption and, from all accounts, 'the lame and sick of Soho' were not entirely innocent.

We have been left a description of these foundations by John Howard (1726–90), the prison reformer, who conducted a survey of most of the hospitals in England in 1789. From the various sets of rules described by Howard, it is clear that the patients were not acutely ill and the so-called nurses seem to have been more like domestics or attendants. There could not have been much nursing at

18 A ward in the Middlesex Hospital at the end of the eighteenth century. Note the wooden beds and the frames for bed curtains. This ward does not look particularly 'offensive' but no doubt in reality it was nearer to John Howard's description than to the artist's imagination.

19 John Howard (1726-90), a social reformer who produced the first modern social surveys. Apart from visiting and documenting all the prisons in Europe, he made a tour of the principal hospitals, to most of which he gave a low rating for hygiene.

St Thomas's, where the patients were allowed out until 8 p.m. in the summer and 7 p.m. in the winter and where, Howard complains, 'the patients easily get out [presumably at any time], there is no proper attention to the gates so that the adjourning gin shops often prevent the efficacy of diet and medicine'.

This efficacious diet consisted of thin gruel for breakfast, six ounces of meat for dinner, but no vegetables, broth for supper and a daily ration of two or three pints of beer. Other rules forbade the inmates to indulge in card playing or dice, pastimes which many of them were apparently well enough to enjoy.

Nor were these new foundations models of hygiene. The wards were long, with the beds in parallel rows, and the rough floors were either washed or 'dry rubbed', which in practice often amounted to hiding the dirt with sand. The wooden bedsteads were covered with mattresses filled with straw or hair, which in some hospitals were infested with bugs. Later, as iron became the vogue, the wooden beds were replaced by the more hygienic iron. In many hospitals the beds were hung with heavy curtains from a semicircular frame above, which must have added to the general 'offensiveness' of which Howard complained so bitterly.

The first nurses often lived out, probably in the adjacent slums. Towards the end of the eighteenth century, they tended to live in; no doubt the governors felt they could control them better that way. The quarters with which they were provided were mean: they slept either in the attics or the basements, or, more often, in what Miss Nightingale later described as 'wooden cages on the landing places outside the doors of wards, where it was impossible for the night nurse to take her rest by day owing to the noise, and where there was not light nor air'.

Not only was the accommodation poor, the pay was low. Although the matrons were paid a salary, the nurses were paid in an infinite variety of cash and kind; in most cases a large part of the wage came in the form of bread and beer, and often very poor beer at that. During the Napoleonic wars (1793–1815), when food was short and prices rising, the nurses of some London hospitals threatened to walk out unless the rations were improved. It is hardly surprising that these early attendants are often accused of taking money offered by the patients and saw little wrong in so doing. What is interesting is that at even this early date there seems to have been a strong ethic, on the part of the governors at least, that the giving of care should be above being done for money.

From Charity to Teaching Hospitals

Although the charity hospitals of the eighteenth century were set up as 'havens of care', it was not long before they changed their purpose. Their foundation coincided with the growth of medical knowledge. William Harvey had discovered the circulation of the blood, dissection was being practised and doctors had a better grasp of anatomy and physiology. There was still little understanding of what caused disease, but at least there were rational theories and some improvements in surgery. In order to improve their techniques the doctors needed practice and material for research; where better to find this than where patients, receiving charity, and therefore unlikely to complain, were under one roof? As their skills improved the doctors acquired a new prestige, and after 1800, when doctors were required to do part of their training in a hospital, there was an increase in young men wanting to be medical students. This led to a further impetus to found more hospitals and in the first three decades of the nineteenth century a number were built, this time not primarily for charity but to provide medical schools in which to train doctors. The medical students paid well and most of the money went to the honorary doctors in the form of fees. These doctors became rich, and this in turn added to the attraction of a medical career.

As medicine became more scientific and treatment more active, the hospitals should have looked for better nurses, but at first the many medical students helped out. They put on poultices and bandages and made the patients comfortable, and spent part of their time on what we would call 'nursing'. However, as more and more patients were admitted for treatment the doctors began to insist on more trustworthy people to supervise the nursing, and some hospitals started to recruit 'sisters'. The new sisters were not promoted 'nurses' but persons drawn from a higher strata of society, perhaps widows in reduced circumstances or women who had been housekeepers in gentlemen's families. They were paid a salary higher than the nurses and usually wore a distinctive uniform, but often they too were partly paid in bread and beer.

At the beginning of Queen Victoria's reign (1837–1901), St Thomas's paid its sisters £37 a year and the nurses £25. At St George's the scale was £21 for sisters and £16 for nurses, but everyone received 'six pounds of bread a week and two pints of table beer daily and a shilling a day for board and wages'. Guy's, in an endeavour to stop nurses accepting money from patients, was more generous: the sisters were paid £50 a year and the nurses £30. Nurses seem to have been paid about the same rate as cotton operatives and sisters rather better than untrained teachers. The Middlesex, while admitting that pay was low, thought there were compensations in as much as the nurses, 'owing to the exemption from laborious employment were enabled to keep a more uniformly neat and cleanly appearance'.

It is commonplace to accept Charles Dickens's Sairey Gamp and Betsey Prig (in *Martin Chuzzlewit*) as typical of nurses in the first half of the nineteenth century, but we must remember that Dickens (1812–70) was a social reformer and the pictures he drew were often caricatures. Undoubtedly there were plenty of slovenly and drunken nurses in bad hospitals, and others who offered themselves for hire outside, but they were only a reflection of the life of the times. Beer and gin drinking to excess were common in all walks of society, but particularly among those for whom the new industrial world offered little comfort and joy. But a picture of universal ignorance and drunkenness is too simple and hardly accords with the hospital records that show rigorous discipline and instant dismissal for such offences as being caught asleep on night duty. There is evidence to suggest that after 1825 nursing in some hospitals was improving; the nurses and sisters who worked closely with the doctors in the teaching hospitals began to absorb their more scientific ideas. Doctors praised the diligence of some sisters and a number became sufficiently confident to help instruct new medical students. Unfortunately not all hospitals were well run and advances in medicine soon began to outpace the gradual improvements in nursing. What was needed now was a training that taught the nurse not only how to perform certain tasks, but also to understand what she was doing and why she was doing it.

The Deaconess Movement

At the beginning of the nineteenth century, a young Lutheran pastor living in Kaiserswerth in Germany became concerned because of the hardship suffered by families where the breadwinner was in prison. Like John Howard 40 years earlier, Pastor Fliedner (1800–64) travelled the continent to study the aftercare of prisoners. In England he met Mrs Elizabeth Fry (1780–1845) and watched her work in Newgate Prison. He was also impressed with new attitudes to care in Holland, where there was an attempt to deal with the vicious circle of poverty, sickness and crime by establishing a system of 'visitors'. Pastor Fliedner returned to Germany convinced that, with the right appeal, a new Protestant organization based on the work of the early deaconesses could be founded.

Back in Kaiserswerth, in 1823, Fliedner and his wife Frederike raised the money to buy a large house to serve as a hospital and the centre of the organization. The new deaconesses were carefully chosen by Frederike, who became the first superintendent of the Kaiserswerth Institute. The life of the deaconesses, like the nuns before them, was one of devotion; they not only looked after the sick in hospitals and in their own homes, but they were also responsible for the cooking, the laundry and the gardening. The sisters nursed, dispensed charity and also undertook what we would call social welfare, but it was always emphasized that spiritual care was as important as physical care. Training included lectures from a physician and a good deal of bible study and practical management. The sisters received no payment, but they were maintained by the Institute and in their old age retired to a house of rest.

The scheme attracted many visitors, one of whom was Mrs Elizabeth Fry, who returned to England determined to establish a similar system. Unfortunately Mrs Fry's work on prison reform and her international reputation left her little time, but with the help of her daughter an Institute of Nursing was eventually founded in Bishopsgate. The nurses, carefully selected, did some hospital work in Guy's, then undertook welfare and nursing work in private houses. Mainly because of the lack of proper training, the mixed aims of the Institute and the fact that the sisters had to perform a variety of duties the scheme made little impact. Nevertheless, the new movement was an impetus to other religious organizations, including the Church of England, to start 'orders of nurses'. But the time for amateur schemes had passed; the new needs of medicine required a more professional approach.

Later, another visitor to Kaiserswerth was the young Florence Nightingale. While she was impressed with the pure devotion of the deaconesses, she quickly decided that 'the nursing was nil and the hygiene horrible.' Miss Nightingale saw the dangers inherent in the Kaiserswerth system and as time went by her forebodings came true.

Although the movement extended to other Protestant countries there were difficulties. Firstly, there were conflicts between the spiritual advisers and the doctors about the main duties of the deaconesses. Secondly, as medicine became more costly it became increasingly difficult to raise money and, in order to keep the costs low, the deaconesses were often overworked and wrongly used. Finally, by the end of the century the scheme was suffering from competition from the professional training started by Miss Nightingale, which was more in keeping with the new aspirations of women and the spirit of the times.

Nevertheless, the Kaiserswerth experiment was important. It was the first purely Protestant appeal to women to place themselves in what was virtually a nursing order. Like St Vincent's Sisters of Charity nearly 200 years earlier, it showed that nursing could be done without vows and that the vocation to care for the sick could be found among women of all classes.

4
Poor Law Nursing

The old Poor Laws allowed parishes to give 'doles' to the needy in their homes and to provide 'workhouses' for the able-bodied paupers. Later, private charity endowed hospitals for the 'poor sick', but as these hospitals became interested in cure they began to exclude those thought to be 'incurable'. This did not matter so much when most people lived in villages, where families looked after their own members and the parish cared for those without family support. But during the eighteenth and early nineteenth centuries many people changed their way of life, moving from the villages to work in the factories in the industrial towns. This movement brought new health and welfare problems; the way these were solved dictated how the poor sick were cared for for the next hundred years.

Changes in Agricultural Life
During the eighteenth century, landlords adopted more scientific methods of farming and men like 'Turnip' Townshend (1674–1738) increased the value of their estates twentyfold in a lifetime. These changes had important consequences. The new methods required capital investment that only the rich could afford, so there were fewer independent farmers, and at the same time the enclosures of common land deprived the poorer people of their smallholdings and grazing rights. But, the most important consequence of the agricultural revolution was greater productivity — more food and better livestock — and this, together with other improvements in living standards, brought about a sharp increase in the population. There were now more workers for fewer jobs and this in turn brought about unemployment and low wages. Matters were made worse by the Napoleonic wars, when supplies from the Continent were cut off; this caused the price of corn to increase and therefore the price of bread, so that the lowly paid agricultural workers were reduced to near starvation. To improve the situation, the magistrates in some agricultural counties devised a scheme for poor relief whereby the labourer's wage could be supplemented out of the poor rate on a scale determined by the price of bread. This scheme, though well intentioned, had the effect of keeping wages low and the price of bread high, and increasing the amount people had to pay in poor rate. The rise

in the rates and the continuing growth of pauperism led many people to question the whole foundation of the Poor Laws and to ponder on whether they were suited to the new economic conditions.

The Industrial Revolution

During the Napoleonic wars and their aftermath, while the agricultural workers were suffering great hardship, the change from hand power to machine power in industry was gathering momentum. As the new industrial towns in the North and the Midlands grew up around what the poet William Blake called 'these dark Satanic mills', land prices rose and hastily built cheap houses were packed together near the factories. At first it was impossible for the unemployed agricultural workers to seek work in the factories because paupers were chargeable to their own parish and labelled 'vagrants' if they left, moveover, until the coming of the railways travel was slow and uncomfortable. So factory owners looked elsewhere for cheap labour; they found it among Irish immigrants, women, children and Poor Law apprentices.

20 *Under the Viaduct* by Gustave Doré. He was drawing attention to the fact that over 100,000 people in London alone had been displaced by the railways, on which they were too poor to travel.

Conditions in the factories were often appalling. Dr Kay-Shuttleworth, a public health reformer, reporting on the Manchester Cotton Operatives in 1832 wrote:

> The operatives are congregated in rooms and workshops during twelve hours a day in an enervating heated atmosphere which is frequently loaded with dust and filaments of cotton, or impure from frequent respiration ... the physical energies are exhausted from incessant toil and imperfect nutrition.

The result of 'this incessant toil and imperfect nutrition' was that factory workers could expect to live barely half as long as workers in the country.

The New Poor Law

The attitude to the poor was influenced by the economic theories of the day and the forecasts of Robert Malthus (1766–1834), who predicted, on very dubious calculations, that the population was rising faster than the country's food supply. If Malthus was right, and many believed him, it was false charity to give relief to paupers who would only then breed more paupers and bring the day of universal starvation nearer. Influenced by these theories, the government passed a Poor Law Amendment Act in 1834, which reversed the policy of giving subsidies to the poor. Instead, paupers were to be offered accommodation in a

21 Illustration from Henry Mayhew's *London Labour and London Poor* (1851). Mayhew (1812-1887) was a playwright and journalist with a gift for making ordinary people talk to him. His vivid reporting of the forgotten urban masses puts him among the great Victorian social reformers.

workhouse where they would be less comfortable and less well fed than the lowest paid worker; it was hoped that this 'workhouse test' would force the able-bodied to look for work in the new industries. In order to keep down the workhouse population, husbands were separated from their wives and children taken from their parents. Within a few years more gaunt, grim, prison-like buildings were erected and the parishes elected Boards of Guardians and appointed 'Overseers of the Poor'. The Act intended that the workhouse test should only apply to those able to work, but the Guardians had neither the money nor the staff to seek out the different categories of pauper and it was easier to put all who were in need of help in the workhouse.

22 A women's dormitory in the new style workhouse. Women and men were separated and all types and conditions herded together. They had to sleep without mattresses.

The Guardians were there to relieve immediate destitution as cheaply as possible; they were not there to deal with sickness, but so often the poor were sick because they were poor, and sometimes they were poor because they were sick. Furthermore, the whole environment of the workhouse was conducive to ill health and the spread of infection. The diet was poor and monotonous and the sanitation primitive with no provision for bedridden patients. In one London workhouse the male inmates slept on the floor while 40 girls shared 13 beds. Above all there was little to occupy the inmates, no amusement or diversion, so that their health was made worse by mental stagnation.

23 Oliver Twist, 'the boy who asked for more', from a drawing by George Cruikshank, who illustrated most of the novels of Dickens.

Charles Dickens wrote *Oliver Twist*, his most famous description of workhouse life, a few years after the new Poor Law which was passed in 1834. This is how he later described a Sunday morning visit to a London workhouse:

The faces were depressed and subdued and wanted colour. Aged people there were in every variety. Mumbling, blear-eyed, spectacled, stupid, deaf, lame; vacantly winking in the gleams of sun that crept through the open doors, from the paved yard; shading their listening ears, or blinking eyes with withered hands.

There were almost 2,000 paupers in this workhouse ranging, Dickens tells us, from 'the infant newly born or not yet come into the world, to the old man dying on his bed'. It was not surprising that by 1861 there were said to be over 50,000 sick people in the workhouses — five times as many patients as in the general 'voluntary' hospitals. In the workhouses, however, where the need was greater, there was no proper medical or nursing care.

The Movement for Workhouse Reform

There was much criticism of the new Poor Laws, and especially their failure to make provision for the care of the sick. The movement for workhouse reform was therefore partly tied up with the campaign for better nursing.

The Guardians, when they did appoint medical officers, paid them badly and often only employed them part-time, so the doctors could do little to improve conditions. However, some — like Dr Rodgers of the Strand Workhouse in

Soho — battled with the authorities on behalf of their charges. Dr Rodgers's main complaint was that the sick were looked after by pauper nurses who were old and feeble, who often could not read and who were quite incapable of carrying out a doctor's instruction. Some 'coughed and trembled all day and were too weak to lift patients in their beds'. These nurses were not paid, but

24 'The Poor House or Pest House'. This title immediately suggests that at least to those forced to enter its doors the workhouse meant disease. Notice that the young, the old, the sick and the well are put together.

FUN.—MARCH 31, 1866.

THE WORKHOUSE MRS. GAMP.

Pauper Nurse:—"SORRY TO DISTURB YOU, MUM, BUT THAT CHILD——"
Superintendent:—"OH, BOTHER THE CHILD! IT'S NO USE ITS BEING ILL WHEN I HAVE A FEW FRIENDS TO TEA!"

25 This cartoon in *Punch* in 1866 suggests that if the workhouse did employ a paid nurse, she was no better than the pauper nurse.

they were sometimes given a glass of beer and 'occasionally for laying out the dead and other specially repulsive duties they had a glass of gin'. They were not above stealing the patients' food and they drank heavily when they could. However, although the general picture of the pauper nurse is one of ignorance and drunkenness, she was not always depraved. Charles Dickens, who had a pretty low opinion of nurses, noted the trust that the wretched and suffering pauper children had in the nurse: 'There was more fellow feeling in the pauper nurses which appeared to make them more kind to their charges than the race of common nurses in hospital.' As St Vincent de Paul had discovered, kindness can come from any walk in life.

As well as the observations of medical officers, reports from the Workhouse Visiting Society remain. In 1853, Louisa Twining, a daughter of the 'Twining Tea' family, visited a 'respectable old lady' who had been forced to go into the Strand Workhouse because she was going blind. Miss Twining, observing the lack of occupation for the workhouse inmates, planned to bring along other ladies to 'read and give instruction'. This idea was quickly banned by the Guardians who did not like 'interfering women': it would be 'an embarrassing and inconvenient precedent'. Opposition made Miss Twining the more determined and eventually, after personal appeals to the Poor Law Board, the visits were allowed to continue 'discreetly' and the Visiting Society was formed. The Workhouse Visiting Society, which continued to the end of the century, and Dr Rodgers's Metropolitan Poor Law Medical Officers Society were both important in bringing about improvements in the workhouses.

The Liverpool Workhouse Infirmary

In 1861, William Rathbone, a wealthy philanthropist who was already in touch with Miss Nightingale about a scheme for district nursing in Liverpool (see page 62), visited the Brownlow Hill Institute. Here he found that the sick endured even greater miseries than those left unattended in their own homes. Mr Rathbone suggested to Miss Nightingale that permission be sought to use trained nurses in part of Brownlow Hill and he would pay the cost. Miss Nightingale, who was interested in workhouse reform, was sympathetic, but permission was difficult to obtain. The Liverpool Guardians did not want outside interference any more than the Strand wanted Miss Twining and her ladies.

Eventually the opposition was overcome and Miss Nightingale selected her 'dearest and best pupil', Agnes Jones, as matron, and promised 12 other nurses from St Thomas's. Agnes Jones, like Miss Nightingale, felt that she had been called by God to nurse and although she prayed that she might not be tested with this ordeal, she accepted the challenge. Miss Nightingale had described Agnes as 'pretty, young, and rich and witty — ideal in her beauty like a Louis XIV shepherdess'. But beneath the beauty was a will of iron.

In 1864, Agnes Jones and her band of nurses took over the female wards at Brownlow Hill. At first there were quarrels and clashes and Miss Nightingale herself had to pour oil on the troubled waters. Then the scene changed; discipline produced a measure of law and order, the drunken pauper nurses were removed and, because of better administration, costs fell. The local people began to sing the praises of the London nurses, the doctors asked for their numbers to be increased and the Guardians were impressed. At last it was agreed that all the wards be put under the control of Miss Jones. Then, in 1868, when victory was in sight, an epidemic of typhus broke out. Miss Jones now had 1,350 patients in her care. The work was overwhelming; she never went to bed before 1.30 a.m. and she was up again at 5.30 a.m. Tired and old beyond her 35 years, she had little resistance and she quickly caught the infection and died. Her last words to Miss Nightingale were, 'You have no idea how overworked I am.'

The death of Agnes Jones was a disaster to the cause of nursing reform in workhouses, but the experiment and the sacrifice were not in vain. From then on the Liverpool scheme was used by reformers to show that the key to order in the workhouses was the separation of the sick and an efficient nursing service.

A New Deal for the Workhouse Sick

Meanwhile, back in London, another blow had been struck for workhouse reform. In 1864, Timothy Daly, a pauper in the Holborn Workhouse, died 'from filth and gross neglect'. It is unlikely that Timothy Daly was the first pauper to die from neglect, but on this occasion the newspapers took up the case as a stick with which to beat the Poor Law Board. Miss Nightingale, quick to seize the opportunity, wrote to the Board telling them about the experiment in Liverpool, and suggested that the Daly case be used to press for sweeping reforms. Mr Villiers, the chairman of the Board, came to see Miss Nightingale, who outlined to him her plan for a reformed nursing service. She made it clear that she felt reform could not take place within the present system: 'The first necessity was to change the mental attitude that made this hideous system possible.'

Miss Nightingale and the more radical reformers wanted separate institutions for the sick, under a single administration for the whole of London and financed out of the general rate. In other words, there should be a national hospital system under central control — something that was not in fact achieved until 1946, when the National Health Service was born. However, in 1866 all seemed hopeful and a bill was prepared to take the sick out of the Poor Law. Then, in February, the Whig government fell from office. This was a cruel blow and the reformers had to start their campaign all over again with the new Tory government. But Mr Gathorne-Hardy, who took Mr Villiers's place, would not accept their plans and he introduced his own bill instead.

The Metropolitan Poor Law Act 1867

The Act introduced by Mr Gathorne-Hardy was a compromise solution: it accepted some of the demands of the reformers but it also upheld the philosophy that paupers must be less comfortable than the lowest paid worker and, sick or well, they must be dealt with *within the Poor Law*. Under the Act parishes were encouraged to group together in larger 'Unions' and to build separate infirmaries for the sick paupers. The Guardians were responsible for the running of the infirmaries and the money was to come from a Metropolitan Poor Fund. The Metropolitan Poor Law Act, as its title suggests, only applied to London, but its principles were quickly copied in the provinces. The new hospitals built by Poor Law Unions were usually called 'infirmaries', but this does not mean that all hopsitals that were once called infirmaries are Poor Law in origin. Infirmary is an old title and was often used by the charity hospitals. The word 'Union' is more telling, and this can often be found in the titles of hospitals built after the 1867 Act. However, the Guardians soon found that new buildings were expensive, so instead they either converted part of the workhouse as an infirmary or upgraded one workhouse in the Union to serve as an infirmary for the group. Many of these hospitals still exist and the plan of the workhouse can often be traced within their walls. By the end of the century there were 22,100 patients in 'separate infirmaries', leaving 36,450 sick still in general mixed workhouses.

Nursing in the New Poor Law Hospitals

By the time the system of separating the sick paupers was established more women were coming into nursing, but as the demand for their services in the general hospitals was increasing there was little hope of repeating the Brownlow Hill experiment on a large scale. All the reformers agreed that the only hope was for the Poor Law hospitals to train their own nurses. At first the Guardians wanted to use paupers as nurses, an idea which was scorned by Miss Nightingale.

26 Reform was slow, and for the 'sick poor' the only hope was to wait in a long queue outside the casualty department of a charity hospital or to be admitted to the workhouse. It is no wonder that of every 1000 babies born, probably 200 died before they were a year old.

Eventually, after pressure from the reform movement, a training scheme was drawn up and in 1873 'probationers' were admitted to train in selected Poor Law hospitals. Progress was slow, especially in the provinces, and in 1879 The Workhouse Nursing Association was formed to press for more and better nurses. By the end of the century, after the Local Government Act of 1888, regulations were passed forbidding the employment of paupers as nurses, but it was still difficult to persuade women to train in a Poor Law hospital because of the old stigma attached to Poor Law institutions. In addition, most of the patients were old and 'chronic' and the work lacked the excitement of the hospitals with operating theatres and surgical nursing. Above all, there were few doctors and no medical students.

However, by the beginning of the twentieth century nursing in the specially built Poor Law hospitals was improving. The first trained nurses had moved on and set up more training schools, so that the hospitals had their own network of nurse training. Meanwhile, the new local authorities had assumed overall control, and as the better hospitals began to admit non-paupers the foundations were laid for the municipal hospital system.

The Workhouse Infirmaries

Although the pauper sick were now getting a better deal, if they were lucky enough to go into a new infirmary, little headway was made where workhouses had merely set aside part of the building as an 'infirmary'. As well as having a depressing atmosphere, they were managed in a different way from the hospitals. Workhouses were run by 'masters' and 'matrons' (often husband and wife), many of whom had little education and no understanding of the needs of the sick. Nurses who had been working in hospitals with doctors and under trained hospital matrons did not easily accept this kind of authority and interference with their work. A textbook of nursing published by Cassell in 1910, while not exactly warning trained nurses off, drops a broad hint as to what they might expect:

> The Superintendent Nurse [in a workhouse] is cautioned that in all matters pertaining to the treatment of the patients she is under the control of the medical officer; she is *in all other matters* bound to recognise as her superior the master or matron of the workhouse. The position of the Superintendent Nurse is therefore one requiring much tact, otherwise there may be, and often is, a good deal of friction between the administrative and medical heads of establishments.

Later in the twentieth century local authorities took over some of the 'mixed workhouses' and converted them into hospitals, but some remained until the National Health Service swept away the last remnants of the Poor Law in 1946. Many of the buildings are still standing with their high windows to prevent patients seeing out and prison-like 'airing courts', to remind us of the way the problem of poverty was dealt with in the nineteenth century.

5
Florence Nightingale
1820-1910

Florence Nightingale belongs to a circle of gifted women who struggled to free themselves from 'lives of busy idleness', to which many Victorian women were subjected. To do this, they often had to battle against their families and fly in the face of tradition. For some, including Miss Nightingale, this meant sacrifice, inner conflict and mental stress.

Born in 1820 of wealthy parents, Florence Nightingale never fitted into the easy-going society life of her day; somehow she felt herself to be different. At the age of 17 she recorded in her private notes that she had received a call from God; what God wanted her to do she was not sure, but it strengthened her notion that she had a special destiny. However, in spite of the call, and the brooding unhappiness of childhood, by the time she was 22 Florence was a prominent figure in intellectual society; she had a surprising degree of learning, was graceful, danced beautifully and was an excellent mimic. Young men fell in love with her, and it was at this time that she met the poet Richard Monckton Milnes, talented, handsome and the heir to a title. Florence, at odds with her mother and sister, was lonely and, longing for affection, was not indifferent to his advances. But, love him as she did, she felt that married life would be a repetition of the useless life she was already leading. In June 1849 she refused him. It was an act that required courage and she wrote in her diary at the end of the year, 'not one day passes without my thinking of him, life is desolate without his sympathy.' At night she dreamed about him. Then, eventually as she sought spiritual consolation, she knew what she must do. She must nurse the sick. The storm burst: her mother raged about 'Florence's ingratitude', her sister Parthe had hysterics and her father retreated to his club.

Fortunately the Nightingales had a wide circle of friends, some of whom realized that Florence had exceptional gifts, and in order to get her away from the scenes at home friends took her to the Continent. While in Germany, Miss Nightingale made her first visit to Kaiserswerth and met Pastor Fliedner; this strengthened her determination to nurse.

Back in England there were endless family quarrels about Florence being made 'to stay at home and do her duty'. Her mother, Fanny, was ambitious and a society hostess, she wanted her younger daughter's help with her incessant round of house parties at the Nightingale country homes and in London. However, the guests were often distinguished, and Lord Ashley, realizing Florence's interest in health matters, suggested that she read the reports of such public health reformers as Edwin Chadwick and Dr Kay-Shuttleworth. Working in secret, she studied every document she could and filled notebook after notebook with masses of facts. A year later, when abroad with her family, she contrived another visit to Kaiserswerth and went round a number of other European hospitals. She was laying the foundations of the knowledge that was to make her Europe's greatest expert on health matters.

27 Florence Nightingale in 1859, from a bust by Sir John Steell. Florence Nightingale hated having her likeness done in any form, but because the non-commissioned officers in the British Army raised a special fund she consented to give her friend, Sir John Steell, two sittings.

By the time she was 30, Florence could count among her friends such people as Elizabeth Browning, George Eliot, Lord Shaftesbury, the poet Arthur Clough and her neighbour, the distinguished statesman, Sidney Herbert; but at home she was treated like a schoolgirl. There were times when she fretted herself to near despair; a desperate cry in a private note at this time reads, 'I see nothing in life but death.' Eventually matters reached crisis point. Her sister Parthe decided to play the adoring sister and follow Florence everywhere, and, if thwarted, she had hysterics. Florence bore this mental persecution with patience and fortitude, and developed an iron self-control that later served her well. At last Parthe's behaviour became so bizarre that the family physician insisted that the sisters be separated, and advised that Florence left home.

Florence was now 32. The Herberts, quick to seize the opportunity, arranged for her to be the Superintendent for the Institution for the Care of Sick Gentlewomen in Distressed Circumstances. Free at last, Florence threw herself into the organization with zest, and while waiting to take up her appointment visited more hospitals, conducted enquiries into hospitals in Europe and spent a month working with the Sisters of Charity in Paris.

It was at this time that she met the novelist Mrs Gaskell (1810-65) who, describing her to a friend, wrote:

> She is tall; very slight, willowy in figure; thick shortish rich brown hair; very delicate colouring, grey eyes which are generally pensive and drooping, but when they choose can be the merriest eyes I ever saw, and perfect teeth making her smile the merriest.

However, Mrs Gaskell was soon to find that beneath that 'excessively gentle voice and manner' there was 'an unbendableness of character', and in spite of the fun and the mimicry 'there was the cold hardness of steel'. Florence went her own way. Her mother said that she had given birth to a wild swan; but in the words of the essayist Lytton Strachey (1880—1930), 'the nightingales had hatched an eagle.'

The Crimean War (1854—6)

In September 1853 Turkey declared war on Russia; England and France, fearful of Russia's intentions, sent fleets to the Black Sea, and war between Russia and England and France followed in March 1854. In September, after much confusion and disaster, the allies landed in the Crimea and besieged Sebastopol. Unfortunately equipment and medical supplies were left behind and, as the winter closed in, the army suffered terrible hardship. This was not the first time military organization had been incompetent, but now the public could read about it. *The Times* had sent out a fiery Irishman, William Howard Russell (1821—1907), as a war correspondent, and his dispatches hit the public like a bolt from the blue. They told generally of muddle, corruption and disaster;

but Russell's most stinging attacks were reserved for the failure of medical organization and the lack of nurses. The French, he pointed out, had their excellent Sisters of Charity.

Sidney Herbert was now secretary-at-war and much of the public indignation fell on his head. He wrote to Miss Nightingale, who was organizing the nursing of cholera patients at the Middlesex Hospital, and asked her if she would take a party of nurses to the British Military Hospital in Turkey.

28 Sidney Herbert, first baron (1810-1861), friend and neighbour of the Nightingale family, and Secretary at War in the Palmerston Ministry during the Crimean War.

By this time, Miss Nightingale had studied Catholic and Protestant nursing orders and, impressed though she was, she did not think them to be the answer to improved nursing. Obedience and devotion were not enough: nurses needed to be educated and trained. With this in mind she set about choosing nurses for the expedition, but the applicants were few and mostly unsuitable. In the end only 14 professional nurses could be found, and the rest of the party was made up from various religious organizations.

On 3 November 1854, the party arrived at the Barrack Hospital at Scutari in Turkey over which, Miss Nightingale said, should have been written 'Abandon hope all ye who enter here.' The hospital itself was a source of infection; the barracks were enormous and built over a dammed-up cesspool from which came a frightful stench, while around the walls there lodged a filthy rabble. The Nightingale party was met by sullen opposition from the doctors in the hospital, who simply refused their help. The first days were a stern test of self-control, for, although patients were dying, Miss Nightingale refused to allow her party to nurse until the doctors asked for them. Meanwhile the nurses spent their time buying equipment, stuffing mattresses, making bandages and cleaning the building.

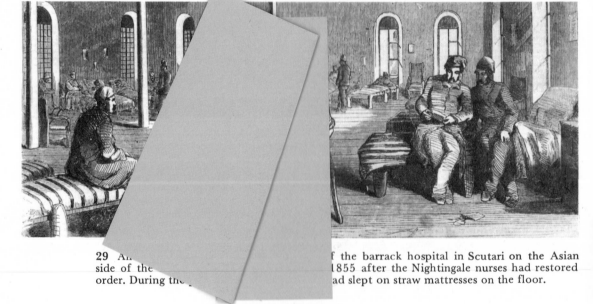

29 A... ...f the barrack hospital in Scutari on the Asian side of the ... ...1855 after the Nightingale nurses had restored order. During the ... ...ad slept on straw mattresses on the floor.

The situation changed with the Battle of Balaclava (25 October 1854). The casualties were enormous and in November the sick, wounded and dying were ferried from the Crimea to the Barrack Hospital. The doctors, overwhelmed, turned to Miss Nightingale. The story of that winter in Scutari is the story of a nightmare; at one time there were over 1,000 cases of Asian cholera — and no toilets. There were four miles of mattresses and beds. The doctors and nurses worked like lions, Miss Nightingale herself would be on her feet for 24 hours on end, or would spend eight hours on her knees dressing wounds. Her influence on everyone was extraordinary; the soldiers described her as 'full of fun' and kissed her shadow. To the army she became a legend. When the soldiers heard she was ill they turned and wept, for Miss Nightingale was one of the first people to recognize that the soldier had a dignity of his own and was not, as the Duke of Wellington had said, 'the scum of the earth enlisted for drink'.

Apart from the strain of nursing, there was also the running of the hospital to be seen to. With the help of Mr MacDonald the administrator of The Times' Fund, Miss Nightingale cut through the army red tape and bought equipment, food and stores in the local market; within a few months they were literally supplying and running the hospital. Then with the aid of Alexis Soyer, a famous chef, she reorganized the feeding arrangements; but although the troops cheered, the officials were resentful and obstructive. However, troubles with the Gift Funds, the doctors and the food were nothing compared with the troubles with the nurses. Some were splendid; but some became ill and Mrs Drake, an excellent nurse from St Thomas's, died. Others became overwrought and had to be sent home, and there were squabbles between the religious groups: some worried about the soldiers' souls rather than their neglected bodies.

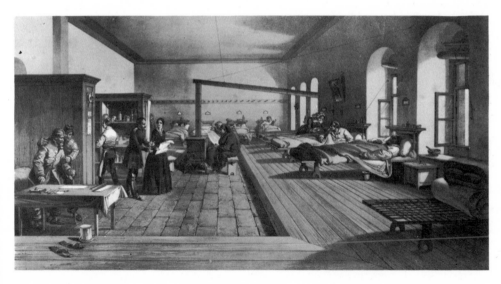

30 Another impression of the wards at Scutari. Now all seems harmony and peace between Florence Nightingale and the doctors. Notice the open windows — Florence was a great believer in fresh air.

The following spring Miss Nightingale crossed to the Crimea, hoping to re-organize the hospitals there, but again she met with official displeasure and was able to achieve little. While in the Crimea she caught 'Crimean fever' and for some time was dangerously ill. However, during her illness she went on writing and assembling facts and figures, by which she was later to show that the high death rate was not due to wounds but to lack of hygiene. She returned to Scutari with a new mission: to improve the lot of the British soldier.

The Royal Sanitary Commission

The Crimean War ended ingloriously in February 1856. Refusing public honour, Florence Nightingale returned home. Wasted and worn out, with her hair cut short like a child's, she longed to lay down the burden; but she knew that the battle had only just begun. Exhausted, she set about asking for a Royal Commission 'to examine the sanitary condition, administration and organization of the barracks and military hospitals and to investigate the administration of the Army Medical Department.' After their first apparent willingness, the government then began to drag their feet; there had already been one disturbing report and they wanted to forget the whole sorry Crimean story. Now, summoning her weary spirit and backed by Queen Victoria and Prince Albert, Miss Nightingale played her trump card. If there was no enquiry, then within three months she would publish her own report. Lord Panmure, the Secretary of State for War, gave in, and the commission began to sit under the chairmanship of Sidney Herbert. Miss Nightingale prepared her own evidence in 1,000 closely printed

31 A sketch of Florence Nightingale made in Scutari in 1856. This was done after her serious attack of Crimean fever, because her hair is cut short.

pages of tables and statistics. Amongst other things she showed that the death rates in army barracks in peace time were twice as high as in the surrounding towns, and the army was supposed to be made up of fit men. The work was enormous and she toiled night and day. Dr Sutherland, one of the commissioners, said:

> Nobody who has not worked with her daily could know her or have any idea of her strength or her clearness of mind, her extraordinary powers combined with her benevolence of spirit; she is one of the most gifted creatures God ever made.

On her return to England Miss Nightingale had taken rooms in the Burlington Hotel and her mother and sister, basking in her national glory, had moved in with her. Suddenly, in August, Florence collapsed. Her condition was serious and her family believed her life was 'hanging by a thread'; Florence also thought that death was near. Whatever the cause of her collapse, Miss Nightingale used her illness to drive out her family and all unwanted visitors. From now on she spent her life confined to bed or couch.

In 1857, a new task presented itself to Florence Nightingale. When the Indian Mutiny broke out on 10 May, she immediately called for a second commission to deal with the shortcomings of the Indian medical service. Once again the work was enormous; not only was she consulted on all matters relating to health and sanitation, but she was also in correspondence with all the great sanitary reformers of the day; at one time there were said to be more papers about the Indian medical service in Miss Nightingale's rooms than there were at the India Office. Ministers, officials and reformers came to see her — by appointment.

The Foundation of the Nightingale School

In 1855 Sidney Herbert had set up a committee and called a public meeting to give thanks for the work of Miss Nightingale in the war. One result of this meeting was that Miss Nightingale had at her disposal the Nightingale Fund with which to start a school of nursing. In 1859 she was consulted about the rebuilding of St Thomas's Hospital where the matron, Mrs Wardroper, was a friend. As her involvement with the hospital grew, she decided to start her scheme there, 'not the best conceivable way of beginning but the best possible.'

However the doctors, like the doctors at Scutari, were opposed to the idea. Mr South, the senior surgeon, declared that 'nurses are in the position of housemaids and only need the simplest instruction.' Because of this atmosphere of hostility, it was essential that the first probationers were carefully selected, for the whole success of the undertaking depended on them. The discipline of the first Nightingale School, therefore, was not discipline for the sake of discipline, but to secure approval for the new system.

Carefully selected pupils of good education and moral standing did a year's training, living in a nurses' home supervised by a 'Home Sister'. This was a new idea: the 'home' was comfortable, with books, maps, music and flowers, and intended to give the pupils a background of culture and education. But, more important, close supervision ensured that no breath of scandal touched the Nightingale ladies. Flirtation meant immediate dismissal.

Although the scheme was intended for any intelligent girl of the right aptitude, it tended to attract the upper classes and two methods of entry soon developed: one for the ordinary pupils who did two years' training and received maintenance and £10 a year and one for the 'lady probationers' who paid for their training. Miss Nightingale was not happy about this division, but the fees helped the finances and the lady probationers tended to show qualities of leadership. In a private letter, she wrote: 'The educated will most likely rise to the post of superintendent, *not* because they are ladies *but* because they are educated'.

The first probationers worked hard, but they were not expected to do domestic duties. 'To scour is a waste of power,' said Miss Nightingale. At first the lectures were simple, but as time went by more and more emphasis was put on the theory of medicine and all nurses were expected to be 'health missioners'. Miss Nightingale herself saw all the pupils; one was sent for interview each day. In this way, she not only knew the nurses personally and made her own, often acid, comments on their record sheets, but she also had a good idea what was being taught.

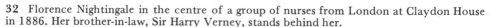

32 Florence Nightingale in the centre of a group of nurses from London at Claydon House in 1886. Her brother-in-law, Sir Harry Verney, stands behind her.

33 Nursing after the Nightingale reforms — one of the wards at the London Hospital in 1888. A definite training was started for nurses in 1874 and after 1880 there were lectures and demonstrations given by the medical staff and the matron.

Once trained, the most promising nurses were sent out to take up appointments and to start new training schools on the lines laid down by Miss Nightingale. It was a 'discipleship' system. The Nightingale matrons were different. They were educated, young and unmarried; often they clashed with the older nurses and the administrators, and in the early years there were many battles. But the new matrons always had an ultimate weapon: they were backed by Miss Nightingale herself. Eventually the new pattern was accepted, and by the end of the century most large voluntary hospitals had a Nightingale matron in charge of both the nursing service and nurse training. Not only was it a matter of prestige for a hospital to have a 'training school', but now they began to compete to produce a longer and even more arduous training and probationer nurses were often exploited.

Later Years

When Miss Nightingale founded the Nightingale Training School in 1860 she was 40, but she considered herself to be old and her life over. In fact she lived for another 50 years, and during this time she worked on all aspects of nursing reform and was a pioneer in health education (see Chapter 6). She became an expert on India, although she never visited the country; she helped the Swiss philanthropist Henri Dunant (1828–1910) with the founding of the International Red Cross; she worked for the reform of the midwifery services; and, as we have seen, she was a moving spirit in Poor Law reform. Moreover, with her flair for figures and statistics she helped to reorganize medical record keeping, so that we have a complete picture of the births, deaths and disease patterns of the late nineteenth century.

The amount of work Florence Nightingale undertook was staggering. How did she do it all? Firstly, she was intelligent, and she was able to pick out and concentrate on only the essential problems — she did not waste time on side issues. Asked to support a children's hospital, she wrote:

> The causes of the enormous child mortality are perfectly well known — want of cleanliness, want of ventilation, careless dieting — the remedies are just as well known and among them is certainly not the establishment of a Child's Hospital.

Secondly, she was an aristocrat and she knew how to manage and lead people. She had personal charm and wit and drew around her a distinguished circle; they came to consult and stayed to do her bidding. But the real secret of the amount of work she managed to get through, apart from sheer willpower, was that she stayed in bed. There was no wasting time in committees or attending deputations in the corridors of power; officials and reformers *came to her*, and stayed only at *her* pleasure. Fortunately for the cause of reform, there was an unending stream of devoted relatives and friends to care for this picturesque, frail invalid and to run her household.

While she was confident that the cause was right, Miss Nightingale had no qualms about sacrificing herself and others 'for the sake of the Work'. When she had doubts then she was filled with remorse and even self-pity. She had said that she 'stood at the altar of murdered men', and her life's work was to see that such preventable suffering never occured again. History absolves her, and as the historian Mrs Cecil Woodham-Smith says, 'Florence Nightingale was the Greatest Victorian of them All.'

6
The Trained Nurse

34 The new style hospital matron. A fashion plate for a matron's uniform appearing in a women's magazine in 1911. The new matrons were often young and smart.

As the new nurses from the Nightingale School at St Thomas's became matrons in other voluntary hospitals, so they in turn started schools of nursing and carried out reforms. St Bartholomew's opened its first school in 1877 and, some years later, one of its first trainees recorded her impressions of the nursing standards before the reforms:

> The staff nurses were chiefly women of the charwoman type with little or no education and few of them with even an elementary knowledge of nursing . . . The worst women we had to deal with were those who used to come in to look after the really bad cases at night. They were mostly dreadful persons possessing neither character nor ability, who used to apply for work much as women now apply for charring.

However, in spite of the 'low character' of some of the nurses, it is clear that many of the older sisters, although lacking in training, had common sense, skill and knowledge. Nor were they slovenly. The writer recollects that the sister of her ward 'always wore a black silk dress when she went round with the visiting physician.'

35 The new style probationer nurse. A new recruit to the London Hospital in 1910. The nurses' uniform was a legacy from the Sisters of the Church and the dress of an upper class servant.

The 'trained' nurses came into the hospitals at the same time as new ideas in medicine, antiseptics and aseptic surgery, and in the next 40 years nursing changed beyond all recognition. The nurses were now the responsibility of a matron who was also a trained nurse, and because there were few other careers open to women nursing became popular and matrons were able to insist on a longer training. The entry requirements were strict and exacting standards became a status symbol for a school of nursing. A good health record was essential and some hospitals insisted on a minimum height and weight. Matrons demanded 'good education and recommendations' and interviews could be formidable. In one famous hospital the would-be recruits were reminded that they 'must be prepared to submit to the discipline of the Guards'.

Many schools had two methods of entry. Lady probationers paid a premium of up to £52 for the privilege of working a 60-hour week and ordinary probationers were paid a 'salary' of £8 to £20 a year. In most hospitals recruits supplied their own uniforms, which could be very expensive. Although probationers worked hard, it is important to remember that most people worked long hours in those days and the miseries sometimes suffered by a young nurse under a harsh sister were no worse than those of pupil teachers or recruits in the army. Young men and women accepted long training and the idea of discipline as the prelude to any career. As for pay, it is difficult to make comparisons; much depended on what was supplied in the way of living conditions. It is customary to think of nurses as badly paid, but the real point is that *all* women received low wages then. However, the ward sister who got £40 a year and her board and accommodation was better off than the secretary in the Civil Service who earned £79 a year, even though, in 1905, it was possible to feed the 'average' family on 23 shillings (£1.15p) a week!

36 The Nurses' Home at the London Hospital in 1908. Notice that music and cultural pursuits were encouraged. Unfortunately not all hospitals provided such good accommodation and facilities.

Most voluntary hospitals followed the Nightingale pattern and provided comfortable nurses' homes. Nurse Hawkins, who started training at Charing Cross in 1905, describes her first few weeks in the school thus:

> I found myself in a cosy room furnished with a bed and a washstand, duchess chest of drawers, a chair and a table. At the end of the corridor there were two bathrooms; hot and cold water abounded, and to add to what seemed the height of comfort was a recess with a kettle (which would boil in less than ten minutes by electricity) if one wanted it.

In 1905 constant hot water *and* an electric kettle must have been luxury indeed, even for a middle-class young lady.

No doubt Cassell's text book for nurses, which was published in 1909 and from which this quote is taken, chose Nurse Hawkins because her comments were favourable. Nevertheless, her description of her first weeks on the wards rings true. Frightened and over-anxious, she found support from the sister and staff nurse, who 'prevented me from taking too much to heart the jibes of my fellow probationers who delighted keenly in making me feel a raw recruit'. As is often the case, fellow workers can be more frightening than authority. From the routine she describes, Nurse Hawkins did little domestic work and spent most of her time with the patients, although it seems that a great deal of effort was spent in getting ready for the visits of the doctors and cleaning up after them.

A nurses' life was not all work. Even though lights were supposed to be out at 10.30 pm, there seems to have been much merrymaking in the nurses' home. Moreover, it sounds as if the nurses were well fed, with 'generous meals' of bacon and eggs, meat, fish and cheese; in 1905 food was still very cheap. However, Miss Hawkins was among the favoured minority, for as we have seen, the nurses in the Poor Law hospitals did not find what seemed to be 'the heights of comfort'.

Nursing in Mental Hospitals

Apart from patients in voluntary hospitals and Poor Law infirmaries, there were also patients in mental hospitals. These were built in the mid-nineteenth century, when the government tried to reform the worst abuses of hospitals such as Bedlam and the private madhouses. The county asylums, the fore-runners of many of our present hospitals, were controlled by the Lunacy Commissioners who insisted on inspection and safeguards. As treatments improved the doctors began to look for a different type of nurse, and as early as 1850 progressive mental hospitals were organizing training schemes. Later a Medico-Psychological Association was formed which in 1891 introduced national examinations for mental nurses.

By the end of the nineteenth century, the 'reformed' system in general

37 The workroom at Bethlehem Hospital in 1860. Even though improvements were made in the mental hospitals during the mid-nineteenth century, it is doubtful if by 1860 the patients were as well occupied as this picture suggests.

hospitals began to be reflected in mental hospitals. Although the nurses in the asylums were few in number and remained under the control of a medical superintendent, it became customary for them to be 'trained' and to rise to the position of 'chief' or 'charge' nurse by merit. Unfortunately, progress was hampered in a number of ways. Firstly, many mentally sick people still languished in workhouses, their condition made worse by poor food and no occupation; however, had they been transferred they would have overwhelmed the staff in the mental hospitals. Secondly, there was a lack of understanding about different types of mental illness. The severe cases that we call 'psychotic', the senile, the depressed and the mild cases were all lumped together, and this as we now know, was the worst thing that could have happened; patients were made more ill by being in hospital. Thirdly, attitudes towards madness changed at the end of the century. There was a wave of public excitement about people being put in asylums so that unscrupulous relatives could inherit their property, and many a Victorian melodrama was written on this theme. The result was that new lunacy laws of 1890 made mental illness 'certifiable'. This was a serious business, involving magistrates; it had the effect of deterring people from seeking help and making mental illness carry a stigma, because 'certified' patients lost their citizenship rights.

As a result of these changes mental nursing became 'custodial', that is, the nurses had to look after large numbers of people for whom there was no treatment and little hope of discharge. Not until well into the twentieth century, with the work of men like Dr Freud (1856-1939), a better understanding of psychology and more rational ways of treating patients, were the mentally sick treated with the same compassion as the physically ill.

District Nursing

In 1861 Mr Rathbone (see page 42), having had the benefit of Nurse Robinson to care for his wife, arranged for her to stay another three months to nurse the poor in a district of Liverpool. Mr Rathbone was one of the many liberal and enlightened reformers who was in touch with Miss Nightingale, and he discussed with her the possibility of using Nightingale trained nurses to care for the sick in their own homes. But Miss Nightingale needed all her first trainees as 'disciples' and as matrons in other hospitals, so she suggested that the city of Liverpool should train its own nurses. The following year, Mr Rathbone generously donated a new building for a school of nursing, and the Liverpool Royal Hospital began to train nurses for work both in hospitals and in the homes of patients. Liverpool was divided into 18 'districts', each with a Ladies' Voluntary Committee responsible for 'giving out medicines and comforts'. A trained nurse who visited the sick in their own homes was attached to each 'district' and was the 'district nurse'.

The following year Mr Rathbone became a Member of Parliament, and, in consultation with Miss Nightingale, started the Metropolitan Nursing Association in London. A scheme was devised by which successful applicants spent a month in a Central Home learning about 'district nursing', then a year in a 'reformed' training hospital, and finally returned to work on the district from the Central Home for another six months. The entry requirements were strict. Miss Nightingale always maintained that the district nurse, because she was on her own, 'would be in a position of greater authority', and therefore needed a long training.

38 The new district nurses. In this cartoon of 1877 these two rather haughty young ladies certainly look very different from Charles Dickens's slovenly Sairey Gamp.

The scheme was a success. Like her counterpart in hospital the new district nurse was an absolute denial of the image of Charles Dickens's Sairey Gamp, and her services were in great demand. In 1877, Queen Victoria, who was always an admirer of Miss Nightingale, gave £70,000 — the greater part of the Womens' Jubilee offering — to extend district nursing schemes. Thus the district nurse became 'The Queen's Jubilee Nurses' and until quite recently district nurses were often known as 'Queen's Nurses'.

Health Visiting

When she was 39 years old, Parthe, Miss Nightingale's sister, married Sir Harry Verney, the head of a distinguished family with a strong interest in social reform. It was in the Verney's historic mansion at Claydon — once famous in the Civil War — that Miss Nightingale spent much of her later life. In 1890, one of Sir Harry's sons was the chairman of the Education Committee for the new local government for North Buckinghamshire; this gave Miss Nightingale the chance to put into practice a long-cherished scheme. With the help of Frederick Verney a training course for lady health visitors was classed as technical education. Miss Nightingale was a firm believer in what was then known as 'the sanitary ideal', which really meant educating people in better habits of health and hygiene. If only this could be done, she declared, she could 'look to the day when there were no nurses to the sick, but only nurses to the well'.

Miss Nightingale was largely responsible for the first course, which consisted of lectures, discussions and practical work with doctors and medical officers of health. It was designed to train a group of people to give support to the district nurse and be concerned with 'the sanitary conditions of persons, clothes, bedding and houses, and the management of the health of adults, women before and after confinement, and of infants and children'.

At first health visiting was considered a separate profession from nursing. Indeed, Frederick Verney wrote: 'The Health Visitor is not a nurse and does not pretend to be one.' However, in the early twentieth century the health visitor's task began to change. Alarming surveys, like Charles Booth's *Life and Labour of the People in London* (1903) and Seebohm Rowntree's *Poverty — A Study in Town Life* (1901), told of the poor health of school children and the appalling death rate among babies. One reason for this ill health was thought to be the lack of knowledge on the part of mothers, and so the health visitor became linked with the 'Maternity and Infant Welfare' movement. As the work tended to concentrate on mothers and babies it became customary to expect the health visitor to have experience in midwifery; thus health visitors were often nurses who later underwent specialized training.

At the beginning of the century, of every 1,000 babies born 156 died before they were a year old. Thanks to better hygiene, improvements in the standard of living and increased medical knowledge, by 1920 this figure was reduced to

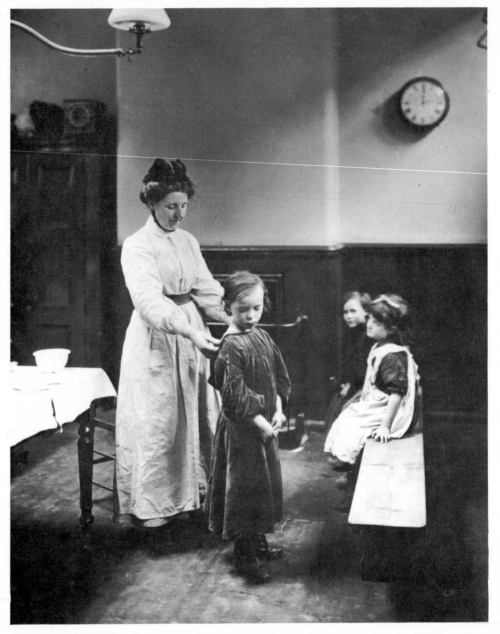

39 Health visiting at the turn of the century. The health visitor examines children for a rash — or probably lice.

60 deaths in every 1,000 live births. This was one of the most dramatic achievements in medical history and, as we shall see in Chapter 9, had far-reaching consequences. It was a success story that was in no small measure due to the work of the early health visitors.

Even in the eighteenth century doctors recognized that the job a man did affected his health. In the late nineteenth century, the new medical officers of health began to show that many industrial processes were dangerous; we have already seen Dr Kay-Shuttleworth's report on the cotton workers of Manchester, who died from inhaling fluff (page 37). People working in factories were likely to have only half the life-expectation of people working in the country. Although government interference in industry was contrary to the economic policies of the day, by the middle of the century Factory Acts had been passed in an effort to control the hours that people worked, but they only touched the fringe of the problem — machinery remained unguarded and industrial diseases were rife. In 1854, in an article called 'Ground in the Mill', Henry Morley protested against the lack of safety precautions in factories: 'There have occurred in the last three years more than 100 such deaths, and more than 10,000 (indeed nearly 12,000) such accidents in our factories, and they are all, or nearly all, preventable.'

Towards the end of the century, some firms began to see the importance of a healthy, accident-free workforce; not only was it more humane, in the long run it was more profitable. In 1872, the Quaker firm of Colmans, realizing the value of healthy workmen, employed a nurse, Phillippa Flowerday, to supervise the health of their employees. Other firms followed Colmans' lead, but the duties of the first 'industrial nurses' tended to be welfare rather than nursing. It was not until the First World War (1914-18) and the increase in the number of women working in factories, that we get the beginnings of a proper medical service in industry.

Nursing in Other Institutions

As well as nursing in hospitals, private homes, industry and in the district, the new trained nurses were also attached to the all-important colonial service and the armed forces.

The army nursing service began in a limited way after the Crimean War (1854—6), when the first female 'trained' nurses were attached to the Army Medical School Hospitals — first at Netley, then at Woolwich. The service was reorganized after the Boer War (1899—1902) under the patronage of Queen Alexandra (wife of Edward VII) and became the Queen Alexandra Imperial Military Nursing Service. A similar service was founded as a Royal Naval Nursing Service. Both services were small and entry was highly competitive, promotion was by an examination conducted by a Nursing Board and service sisters had to take a special course in administration. Many applied but few were chosen. The service was backed up by a Territorial Force Nursing Service, 'which will be mobilized in the event of the invasion of this country'. Written in a nursing textbook in 1910, this gives some idea of the 'expectancy of war' at that time.

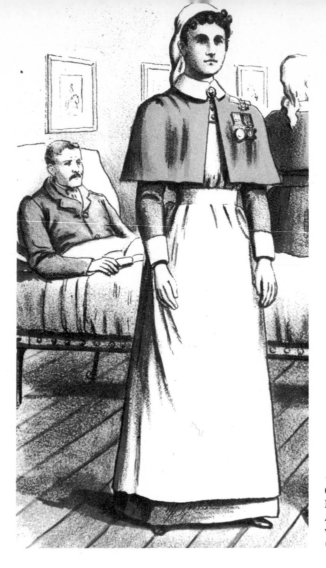

40 The uniform of the Queen Alexandra Imperial Nursing Service (1897). Army nursing sisters still wear a grey and red cape (see also picture 52).

After the First World War, when the Royal Flying Corps became the Royal Air Force, it developed its own medical service to which was attached the Princess Mary Royal Air Force Nursing Service. This was a small corps of specially selected trained nurses who wore the air-force blue uniform with a distinctive black tricorn hat — known irreverently by the wearers as a 'Dick Turpin'.

In the 50 years between the founding of the Nightingale School and the First World War, nursing had been transformed. From being the task of a devoted attendant, or an occupation for a woman of 'low character', it was now a profession offering a wide range of opportunities to educated women.

7
Nursing becomes a Profession

The Dispute about Registration

In 1881, at the age of 24 and typical of the new style of 'lady' nurse, Ethel Gordon Manson became the matron of St Bartholomew's Hospital. The daughter of an MP, she was gifted, rich and articulate. While matron at St Bartholomew's she initiated changes in and lengthened the training of nurses; at the same time, she became convinced that something should be done to safeguard the title 'nurse', for in spite of the reforms anyone could still call themselves a 'nurse'. So Miss Manson started to campaign for nurses to be 'registered' in the same way as doctors. In 1887 she married Dr Bedford Fenwick, who shared her views, and she retired from active nursing to devote the rest of her long life to the suffragette movement and nursing politics.

41 Mrs Ethel Bedford Fenwick as a young woman. As Ethel Gordon Manson she became the matron of St. Bartholomew's at the age of 24 (1881).

The first step was to form an organization to lobby Parliament to introduce a law to control nursing and limit it to 'registered' nurses only. The nurses who supported Mrs Bedford Fenwick joined the British Nurses' Association, but by no means everyone agreed with their forcibly expressed views. Florence Nightingale, for instance, who was still active behind the scenes, thought the profession was too young to be standardized and was suspicious of the 'stiff examinations and high registration fee' the Bedford Fenwicks were proposing. 'Nursing has to do with living bodies and spirits. It cannot be tested by public examination, though it may be tested by current supervision,' she wrote.

Miss Nightingale was not opposed to registration in principle (she thought the profession might be ready for it in about 40 years), but she was strongly opposed to the rigid controls proposed by the 'Fenwickites'. Other opposition came from hospital administrators, who saw nurses becoming too powerful, and some doctors thought that 'newfangled registered nurses' would take away some of their livelihood. Moreover, the situation was complicated by the outspoken public utterances of Mrs Bedford Fenwick and her work with militant suffragettes. In what she called 'a trumpet call to arms', she declared that 'the Nurse Question is the Woman Question.' In her enthusiasm the two campaigns became mixed and this alienated some of her supporters.

The controversy about registration was bitter and often personal. Mrs Bedford Fenwick started and edited a journal called *The Record,* which was used to promote the cause of registration and abuse its opponents. These replied with equal abuse in other journals. Miss Nightingale, who kept out of the conflict, became fearful that the profession would be split in two, rather in the way families had been split over the Reform Bill (1831) when she was a child.

In 1902, because of the concern about the deaths of women in childbirth, it was decided that midwives should be 'registered' with a central board. Although the reason for registering midwives was hardly the same as the Fenwickites had for wanting to register nurses, they saw this as an opportunity. Re-rallying their forces, they persuaded the government to set up a committee to investigate the registration of nurses. The findings of the committee were disappointing: it agreed in principle with registration but recommended *two* registers — one for those with a complete training and one for the less highly trained — a proposal which was eventually implemented nearly 40 years later. But as the dispute about registration continued, the clouds of war gathered over Europe and, with more urgent business on its hands, the government dropped the discussion on nurse registration.

There were 2,000,000 casualties on the Western Front. As the muddy trench warfare of Flanders produced its terrible toll of wounded, more and more nurses were sent to France. The small Army Nursing Service quickly called up territorials, creating great shortages at home. In 1914 there was no Ministry of Health and no one had overall control of the hospitals. However, the British Red Cross, which had been founded in 1870, now linked with the Order of St John of Jerusalem to form a Joint War Committee. This committee, with its tremendous prestige and resources became an important force. Since 1909 the British Red Cross had been building up Voluntary Aid Detachments, and at the outbreak of war there were 80,000 auxiliaries ready to work in hospitals. Now, as the casualties mounted, the hospitals were flooded with volunteers who had to be fitted into the existing staff. Some VADs had had a good training, others had not. The situation was complicated by the fact that there was a tendency for VADs to come from the upper classes and some of these expected to take precedence over the trained nurses. But by now most trained nurses from the better hospitals had done a three-year course and they were suspicious about the short courses for VADs. Inevitably, quarrels broke out and from time to time there was open conflict. Nursing journals wrote scathingly about 'ignorant amateurs', and were fearful lest VADs posed as 'trained'

42 British army nurses arriving at Le Havre in 1914, grouped beneath a statue of Joan of Arc. Within a few months these nurses would be facing the horrors of the casualties of trench warfare.

43 Queen Mary talking to the matron of an army hospital in Boulogne just before the 1917 summer offensive and the battle of Passchendaele.

44 Nursing the wounded in a makeshift hospital in Flanders. Nurses had to work with little equipment and often under terrible conditions.

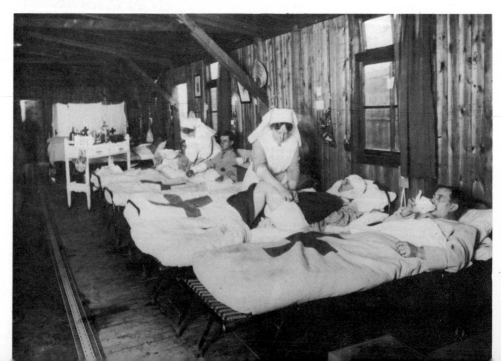

45 A rather sad picture of a VAD nurse — presumably the letter contains bad news. Ten million men died in the 1914-18 war, and of these about one million came from the British Empire.

nurses after the war. But perhaps the greatest cause of friction was the fact that some VADs used social influence to get themselves to France, to nurse the sick and wounded. 'Young women with their "express training" assuming full nurses uniform with the addition of a red cross are treated by medical men and society people as trained nurses,' commented the *British Nurses' Journal* in July 1914.

The trained nurses, as we have seen were not particularly united, but they were determined that their hard-won position was not going to be usurped by 'society amateurs'. But VADs were not the only problem. With patriotic fervour, nurses with previous training returned as volunteers. Some had certificates, some had not; who was to say what was the value of the certificates?

The task of sorting out these difficulties fell to the Joint War Committee, who became convinced that there must be some accepted safeguards for the public and the profession. The issue of registration had become deadlocked in personal feuds and interests and this could only be broken by initiative from another source.

46 Nurse Edith Cavell was the matron of the Red Cross Hospital in Brussels when it was occupied by the Germans. She continued to nurse all nationalities, but because she helped British soldiers to escape, in the spring of 1915 she was rather hastily shot as a spy by the Germans.

The war had brought many changes. Women had played an important part and by the middle of the war it was clear they would get the vote. The nation had been stirred by the devotion and sacrifices of women like Edith Cavell, the Red Cross nurse who had been shot by the Germans in 1915. In nursing itself old traditions had been shaken, nurses had had to adapt to new conditions and, in spite of conflicts, professionals and amateurs had worked together — often to mutual benefit. There had been a new spirit in which people had accepted change for the sake of unity in the war effort. With remarkably clear sight the Joint War Committee set out to exploit this unity with a proposal for a new type of organization.

At this time, the matron-in-chief of the Red Cross was Dame Sarah Swift, previously matron of Guy's Hospital. Dame Sarah was not involved in the registration controversy and she now discussed with the Hon. Arthur Stanley, the distinguished Chairman of the War Committee, the idea of starting a 'College of Nursing' on the lines of the Royal College of Physicians and Surgeons. A tactful letter was sent to all training hospitals pointing out that, although there was no general agreement about registration, something needed to be done to co-ordinate nursing opinion. The letter suggested that all trained nurses unite in one democratic organization with the power in the hands of the membership. Nurses were being offered an organization to give them a say in their own affairs.

Just as the time had been ripe for Miss Nightingale to found nursing as a profession, so now the time was ripe for the profession to conduct its own affairs. The College was founded in April 1916:

> To provide a uniform standard of training . . . to improve the quality of Nursing Service and the conditions under which nurses work, to assist in securing State Registration for nurses, and to further in every possible way the advancement of the profession through legislation, post-graduate study — theoretical and practical — scholarships and specialization.

47 Dame Sarah Swift, CBE, RRC, was the matron of Guy's Hospital from 1901 to 1909. With great tact and wisdom she helped to sort out the problems of the Red Cross Society. In 1916, she founded the College of Nursing.

Considering that it was the middle of the war, the response was enormous and by 1918 there were 13,000 members. They elected a Council of Nurses, appointed officers and set up 'centres' — later to be called 'branches' — throughout the country, through which the views of nurses were aired. It was thought that this new democratic organization would be responsible for registration, but it was not to be. Soon the old quarrels broke out again; Mrs Bedford Fenwick, still active, did not agree with the broader approach of the College, and she and her supporters started to lobby Parliament with their own scheme for limited and strict registration. As the profession was clearly divided and could not agree amongst themselves, the newly formed Ministry of Health intervened and in 1919, Dr Addison, the first Minister of Health, drew up the first Nurses' Bill. Thus, by disagreement, the nurses lost the chance of keeping policy about their training and registration in their own hands.

The General Nursing Councils

In December 1919 the Nurses' Bill received Royal assent. A General Nursing Council for England and Wales and subsequently Councils for Scotland and for Northern Ireland were set up. The Councils had a duty to keep a register of nurses who had received general training, and also a number of supplementary registers for nurses who were only trained in one branch of nursing, such as 'fever' nursing or the 'nursing of sick children'. The College did not agree with the idea of supplementary registers and maintained that all nurses should do a 'comprehensive basic training' first and then, like doctors, specialize later. This remained the policy of the Council of the College and was the cornerstone of most of the later reports on the reform of nurses' training (see Chapter 9).

The main duties of the General Nursing Council were to compile a syllabus and subjects for examinations and to keep a register. Then in 1921, in common with other professions, the Council set up a Disciplinary Committee which gave it the power to take off the register the name of any nurse who was found to be 'not a fit and proper person to be called "nurse"'.

The early days of the Council were stormy. There was disagreement between the government and the profession about the requirements for 'basic' training; there were disputes about who should be appointed or elected to the Council, the standard required for registration and the hospitals that should be accepted as training hospitals. Most hospitals wanted to be recognized by the Council, for this not only gave them a status, but also meant that they could recruit probationers who were cheap labour.

In 1925 the first examinations were held and the Councils settled down to a more peaceful existence. Since then, the only way of becoming a state registered nurse has been by doing a three-year training in an approved hospital or group of hospitals, and by passing the written and practical examinations conducted by the General Nursing Council.

Further Education for Nurses

The College had *not* become the nurses' registering body and the ultimate control of nurses' training had passed to Parliament. The Council of the College now had to become the watchdog for the profession. It was soon clear that the new registration would provide only a minimum standard: there would be many nurses capable of, and whose jobs required, a more demanding education. Therefore, the first task of the College was to set up an Education Department, with links with universities. The most important need was to educate the teachers of nurses and, as early as 1918, a course was arranged with the University of London, which later awarded a Diploma. As well as some nurses needing higher education, there were those who needed special courses. Nurses were now working in all branches of public health, schools, factories, private houses and, at a time when there was still a British Empire, they were also in great demand overseas where they faced health problems very different from those in England. At the same time, the work of the health visitor was changing and she needed a course with a different emphasis in order to be able to cope with the growing work with mothers and babies. The new College tried to respond to the various needs, organize courses and recommend to the government the certificates that should be required before nurses took up specialized or advanced posts.

48 Nurses studying in the old College of Nursing Library before it moved to its present premises in Cavendish Square, London.

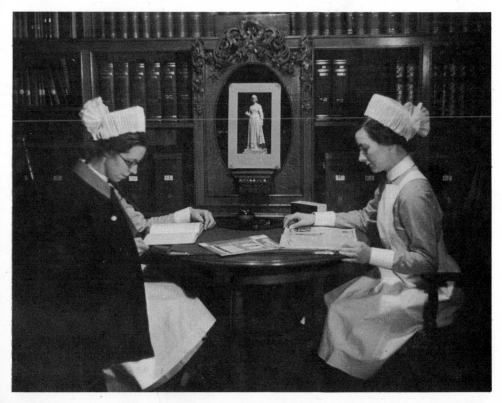

By 1928, because of its contribution to education, the College was incorporated by Royal Charter and in 1939 it became 'The Royal College of Nursing' — now often known as the RCN. The Education Department has become the Institute of Advanced Nursing Education. Many courses once pioneered by the College are now undertaken by technical and other colleges, and although the College still conducts its own courses, its main functions now are advising and controlling the institutions which run nursing courses and instituting research.

Nursing as an Organized Profession

When Miss Nightingale founded a 'training school for nurses', she changed nursing from a vocation for some, and a job for others, into a profession. It was a profession because the main characteristics of a profession are 'a long training and a code of ethics' — which nurses now had. But a profession has other hallmarks, and some of these were absent. Nurses were not controlling their standards and were not defining what was and what was not nursing; nor were they, like doctors, represented on governing bodies. Above all they were not joining together to build up knowledge about nursing. To become a full profession, nurses had to form an association that would collect and disseminate nursing knowledge and act as a forum for nursing opinion.

This 'professional organization' became the other side of the work of the new College. The membership was arranged so that all nurses could contribute opinions and exchange ideas. To do this, meetings and conferences were promoted and the resolutions were passed on to the government. In 1922 a Library of Nursing was opened which, thanks to endowments, became the largest nursing library in Europe. In order to help professional nurses keep up to date with the latest techniques in nursing, the College also began to cooperate with a publishing firm to produce the weekly professional journal *Nursing Times*.

In 1925 probationer nurses, or student nurses as they were now being called, joined together to form a Student Nurses' Association. The students were concerned with the exploitation of nurses in training, who by now had often become the main labour force in hospitals. In its efforts to get a better training system, the Association affiliated itself with the College of Nursing and had its headquarters in the College building. Recently the Association has become an integral part of the Royal College of Nursing.

As the membership of the College grew, new departments were set up: some dealt with the special needs of nurses in such fields as public health and nursing in industry, while others grew up to look after the general needs of nurses, negotiating salaries and conditions of service and giving advice on legal matters. As the health service grew more complex and as nurses began to play a fuller and more important role in all aspects of health care, so they, in turn, needed more services to help them.

8

Nursing and the National Health Service

Hospitals in Difficulty

In the period between the two World Wars (1918-39) it was not uncommon to see voluntary hospitals with hoardings outside saying, 'Half a million pounds needed urgently. Please give generously.' The reason for this was that medical costs were rising, a higher standard was expected by patients and a severe economic slump in the 1920s and 1930s had caused a fall in donations. To overcome the difficulties, hospitals began to open private wings and to charge patients according to their means. Sometimes the charge was quite

49 School children help to collect money for hospitals. In 1936 Rhoda Reynolds collected £26 12s 4d for the Royal Hospital, Richmond, and was made the youngest honorary life governor. Today, Rhoda's £26 would be worth over £200.

heavy and the middle classes started taking out insurances against hospital costs. At the same time the old Poor Law hospitals, now run by local authorities and paid for out of the rates, were in similar difficulties. With high unemployment there were many defaults on the rates, and in some depressed areas hospitals were so poor that all the sheets were patched and sometimes there was hardly a sound pillow case to be found.

50 This picture was taken to show midwives taking out the new portable pain-relieving apparatus strapped to their auto-cycles. However, the background is a piece of 'unwitting testimony' and reminds us that in the 1930s all the voluntary hospitals were begging for money.

One effect of the economic slump was that although the cost of living had doubled in the First World War, hospitals were still paying nurses the same salaries. A ward sister in 1930 received £60 to £70 a year, probably only £20 more than the salary received by a ward sister in 1900. However, because of high unemployment, the difficulty of getting into university and the shortage of careers for girls, there were plenty of volunteers for nursing. Yet in spite of brisk recruitment, hospitals were still short-staffed because of the increasing use of hospitals. Many nurses left their training because of bad pay and conditions and because they were dissatisfied with the training arrangements. A

number of people thought that the only solution to this dilemma was for the
government to become partly responsible for the cost of training nurses and
doctors. But there was a strong body of opinion who feared that if this happened the government would 'nationalize' the hospitals and doctors would
lose their professional independence. As hospital costs rose and the shortages
grew worse, the debate widened, but before any action could be taken the
Second World War broke out.

51 Nurse setting out to attend to patients injured by a V2 rocket
attack in London's Farringdon market in 1945.

The Second World War (1939—45)

Like the First World War, the war from 1939-45 threw a great strain on the hospital services. Everyone feared massive aerial bombardment with thousands of civilian casualties. It˙was thought that 67,000 nurses would be needed just to man the first aid posts and there were, at that time, only 46,000 trained nurses known to be working. To cope with the expected demand the govern-ment set up a Civil Nursing Reserve, which people with hospital experience were invited to join. Just as in the First World War there was difficulty in sorting out the nurses who called themselves 'trained', now there was trouble over those who claimed to have experience and be 'assistant nursès'. This led the College of Nursing and the government to the conclusion that a second type of trained nurse was needed, one with a shorter and more practical pre-paration. The suggestion was by no means universally acceptable to trained nurses, and the nursing journals were full of critical letters. But the government were now paying the Civil Nursing Reserve and it was important that those with experience be paid a suitable salary. For this reason, in 1943, another Nurses' Act was passed which allowed the General Nursing Council to keep a 'roll' of nurses with appropriate experience. After the initial enrolment new assistant nurses were required to take an assessment test. The new 'enrolled nurse' quickly proved a valuable member of the nursing team, although it was many years before her contribution was fully recognized.

Another change brought about by the war was the way nurses were paid. Before the war each hospital had its own rate of pay, but with the government now paying some 20,000 nurses in the Reserve something had to be done to standardize salaries. Nurses were not slow to exploit the government's dilemma and in October 1941 for the first time in history, their representatives sat down with government officials and negotiated what was to become a national salary scale. The result was an improvement in pay, and since 1945 all nurses in the health service have been paid according to national scales.

Nursing in the Services

As the war wore on and extended to the Middle and Far East, more and more nurses were required for the three nursing services of the Crown. This was 'total' war and there was no question of women being kept in 'protected' positions — even hospital ships were torpedoed. The versatility and ingenuity of nurses was tested as never before. Some manned advanced casualty stations close to the enemy lines; some worked in the jungle making their own hospitals in clearings; some were in the desert where water was rationed and sand blew into everything. Many became adept at helping with operations by the light of hurricane lamps and sterilizing instruments on old primus stoves; others were expert at equipping hospitals from captured enemy property and making furniture from packing cases. In the Air Force sisters were trained to make parachute jumps, while Army nursing sisters were some of the first to help

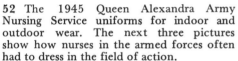

52 The 1945 Queen Alexandra Army Nursing Service uniforms for indoor and outdoor wear. The next three pictures show how nurses in the armed forces often had to dress in the field of action.

53 Towards the end of the Second World War certain sisters in the Royal Air Force Nursing Service were specially trained to make parachute jumps so that they could be landed at advance casualty stations.

the survivors of the notorious Belsen concentration camp. The traditional uniform, so long the pride of nursing sisters, was often exchanged for battle dress and khaki trousers — a practice not always approved by the authorities. If women had to prove themselves in the First World War, they did so all over again in the Second.

At the same time, the needs of war revolutionized medicine and, subsequently, nursing. Before the war there was no defence against such infections as pneumonia and septicaemia; by 1945 the use of antibiotics like penicillin had completely changed the nursing of patients with virulent infections. The 'miracle' drug could cure in a few days. Doctors often had to allow their patients to get up and return to the war quickly, and it was found that they came to no harm; in fact they often had fewer complications than the patients who stayed in bed. Before the war the death rate from severe burns was high; during the war it was found that sailors who were badly burnt when their ship was torpedoed recovered more quickly and had less scarring if they had been flung in the sea and soaked in sea water for hours. All the time the medical people were finding faster and better ways of curing patients. By the end of the war new methods and drugs had completely revolutionized the hospital ward. Instead of two rows of tidy beds with the same group of patients confined to them for weeks, the ward was a constant sea of comings and goings.

54 *left* An Air Force Nursing Sister copes with the realities of supplies dropped by parachute. Dropping equipment and personnel by parachute is useful when dealing with remote country without roads or landing strips.

55 *above* An Army Nursing Sister in charge of the wounded on a flight back from Normandy in 1944.

Beveridge and the National Health Service

The upheavals of war not only showed up deficiencies in the health service, but also unmet needs in the social services. Early in the war, a committee under the chairmanship of Sir William Beveridge (1879-1963) was set up to make a plan for the future. The Beveridge Report set out to deal with the five giants that destroyed people — Want, Disease, Ignorance, Squalor and Idleness — by making a 'contract' between the state and the individual. During their working life everyone would contribute to a National Insurance Fund, and when they were unable to work because of sickness, unemployment, injury or old age they would receive certain flat-rate benefits as of right. The success of the plan depended on a number of interlocking services, one of which was a National Health Service.

Unfortunately, the early plans for a National Health Service produced bitter criticism from the doctors and from local governments. The doctors were afraid they would be controlled by the State and the local authorities resented losing their hospitals. Because of this controversy, the Health Service when it did come was not as revolutionary as it might have been. In order to placate everyone involved the Minister of Health, Aneurin Bevan (1897–1960), took over all the health services and then handed them back for their day-to-day running to the people who had administered them before. The main difference was that all services were now paid for out of central funds and treatment was 'free'. Of course, the services were not 'free', people were

56 A meeting of the British Medical Association in 1944. The Secretary, Dr Charles Hill (later Lord Hill), is second from the right. It was at this meeting that the doctors rejected the government's plan for a National Health Service.

paying insurance stamps, but they were now paying while they were well.

The services were divided into three. The hospitals were run by Regional Boards responsible for all but the teaching hospitals, and this led to a big improvement in the old Poor Law hospitals and a new demand for nurses. The general practitioners were financed separately and were responsible to an Executive Committee. And the local authorities, while losing their hospitals, kept control of the 'community health services', so district nurses and health visitors still worked with medical officers of health from the Town or County Hall (see Chapter 9).

One important change was that all hospitals were now grouped together and the traditional divisions began to disappear. At the same time there was a fall in the number of people with infectious diseases, for example during the war, at any one time there were about 30,000 patients in hospital with tuberculosis; by 1948 the figure was negligible. The control of infection meant that fever hospitals and sanatoria could be released for other purposes; beds were re-allocated, sometimes for acute work but often for the long term patients. These changes had consequences for nurses, fever nursing was no longer import-ant and schools of nursing had to be based on a group of hospitals in order that students could have a wide enough experience.

Divisions in the Health Services
Before the war some nurses worked for voluntary hospitals, some for local government and others for private institutions. Now nurses were divided by what they did. All hospital nurses worked for one authority, all community nurses for another; those working to prevent illness were divorced from those working to cure illness. These divisions had a number of unfortunate effects. Firstly, there was little communication between the different branches, some-times there were gaps in the care of patients and at other times there were two groups looking after the same patient. Secondly, the division had a bad

effect on the training of nurses and doctors who knew little about health care in the community. Thirdly, the divisions made the service expensive: patients were in hospital who would have been better in a community hostel had there been money from the rates to provide one. As the costs rose, people began to argue that the health services should be reorganized and placed under one authority. As a result, since 1974, all nurses in the National Health Service have worked for an Area Health Authority, which usually covers the same area as a county or metropolitan area.

Changes in Nursing in the National Health Service

Once the National Health Service was established, more people used it and this meant an increase in the demand for nurses. At the same time, advances in medical knowledge enabled more to be done and people expected more, and of course some techniques, such as transplants, required a high ratio of nursing staff. But as more nurses were required, fewer were available. During the 1930s the birth rate had been low and now there was comparatively fewer girls aged 18 in the population. Because there were more boys than girls and there was full employment, marriage started taking place earlier. And for those who did not marry, there was a wide choice of careers.

Traditionally, since the Nightingale reforms, student nurses had been young, unmarried girls mainly from the United Kingdom. Now thought had to be given to attracting other groups. Campaigns were launched to attract married women back to nursing, and part-time employment — once unheard of — became common. Although there had always been men in nursing, indeed many of the religious orders had been nursing brothers, they had played little part in the reformed nursing. Now recruitment was aimed at attracting men as student nurses, and since the war their numbers have doubled. But still there were not enough nurses, so more were recruited from overseas, some of whom — once they were trained — returned to their country of origin to nurse there.

If more nurses could not be found, then the answer was to use those we had with greater care. With the help of management experts many of the purely routine nursing tasks have been dropped: jobs that were once part of the nurse's day, such as preparing patients' diets, are now done by other people, and ward clerks, receptionists, catering staff, domestic supervisors and many others help to relieve nurses of non-nursing tasks. On the other hand, new medical techniques mean that nurses have to learn new skills and manage complicated machinery. Nursing does not stand still; as doctors take on new tasks, so the jobs *they* once did pass to nurses. But in this changing world nurses have to decide what is nursing and what is not. Nursing is not a series of jobs to be done, and medical techniques are not always nursing. Nursing is caring for people as separate individuals and seeing and understanding the problems and suffering of each person. In this respect, nursing is the same today as it was in the Middle Ages.

9
Nursing Today

Changing Demands for Health Care
Although the principles in caring for the sick do not change, the modern nurse faces problems very different from those that met her predecessors.

In the nineteenth century the main cause of death, especially among children and young people, was infectious disease. At that time there were no microscopes powerful enough to detect the disease-producing bacteria, but doctors and sanitary reformers knew from experience that poor hygiene made people susceptible to infection. So reformers set out to improve the water supply and public hygiene, and as sanitation improved, so the great epidemics of cholera and typhoid abated.

In 1880 Robert Koch (1843–1910) discovered the tubercle bacillus; at last doctors knew that bacteria were the true cause of infectious disease. Once the bacteria for each disease was identified, it was often possible to produce 'antitoxins' and immunize people against diseases like diphtheria and scarlet fever. This, together with the strict isolation of fever victims and their contacts, led to a dramatic fall in the number of cases and deaths.

Although the doctors were successful in dealing with infectious diseases, there was still little defence against such infection as wound sepsis and septicaemia. Then in the 1930s, Alexander Fleming discovered that 'a good microbe could drive out a disease producing microbe.' He called this first discovery 'penicillin', because it was produced on a brush-like mould called 'penicillium'. Once the principle was established more powerful drugs, later called 'antibiotics' were produced and with a few notable exceptions, such as the common cold, the conquest of infection was complete. Within the space of 60 years the disease producing bacteria — the greatest killer of man — had been defeated. This has had an enormous effect on the size of the population, the density of age groups within it and the health problems that they face.

In the nineteenth century, most of the population was young. The novels of Charles Dickens are full of children: many are orphans because their mothers died of infection in childbirth; others, like Little Nell, die young. In the mid-nineteenth century, thirty per cent of the population died before the age of 20 and few lived to be old. Now, because babies and children rarely die people do not need to have large families to replace the population. Moreover, children are no longer needed as labour or to support parents in their old age, and the tendency is for the birth rate to fall. Nevertheless, the population is growing, because people are living longer. In 1900 there were only one and a half million people past the age of retirement, now there are over nine million.

These changes are very important for the work of nurses. We have exchanged old health problems for new, and by conquering bacteria we have opened Pandora's box. In the nineteenth century only the fit survived; now the frail and the handicapped are all kept alive, and as they grow older they often need more and more care. Secondly, people now live to ages when the way they have lived and the risks to which they have been exposed — such as smoking, alcohol, drugs and chemical pollution — all begin to tell. Thirdly, old people have more health problems because parts of their 'machine' begin to wear out. So now, instead of infectious diseases, we have to deal with the various cancers that are more common after middle age, heart disease, the 'wearing out' of the blood vessels and disabling conditions like arthritis. We are faced with the paradox that although people are healthier, they need more care and therefore more nurses.

57 The best 'first aid' is rapid transport. A nursing sister accompanies a severely injured patient on a journey by a specially equipped ambulance to a hospital with an Intensive Care Unit.

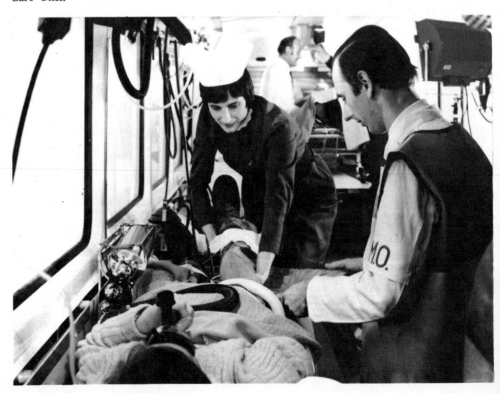

In the last few decades the work of nurses has changed because of progress in medical techniques and knowledge. There have been advances on two main fronts. Firstly, because of more scientific knowledge and new medical machinery, doctors are able to intervene after an accident, be it road accident or heart failure. Sometimes the patient can be resuscitated and kept alive on complex machinery. Patients whose kidneys fail may be saved by 'dialysis', that is by using a machine to do the work of the kidneys. Those whose breathing has stopped — possibly because the muscles are paralysed, as in poliomyelitis — can be made to breathe artificially on a lung machine. At the same time, because of improvements in anaesthetics and surgery, it is possible to contemplate operations on the heart, or organ transplants, unheard of 20 years ago. To practise these advanced techniques the doctors require skilled assistants.

The other front on which progress has been made is in keeping people alive longer and in improving the quality of life for those with disabilities. This is partly due to new and powerful drugs, but largely because of new regimes for patients. Years ago patients were kept in bed; now they are got up and encouraged to be independent as soon as possible.

Apart from new surgery, machines and regimes, doctors today are more concerned with the psychological background of many of the ills from which people suffer, particularly those related to the stress of modern life. Over two thousand years ago, the Greeks said there should not be two different doctors,

58 The modern operating theatre. The theatre sister carries the heavy responsibility of ensuring that everything is ready for the surgeons and of assisting them during the operation.

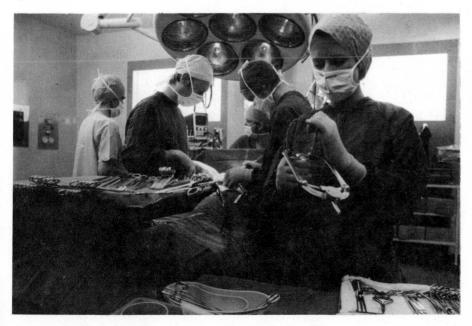

one for the body and one for the mind, but rather one doctor for both. This wise saying is more than ever true today; to understand illness it is necessary to know the patient, his family, the way he lives and works and the worries that beset him. But all this is more time-consuming than just handing out a bottle of medicine.

Adapting Nurses' Training to New Needs

Because of all these changes it has been necessary to modify nursing education. Nurses are now needed with different skills and the training for the register and roll has changed accordingly. Less attention is given to hygiene and sanitation and more to psychology, less time to infectious diseases and more to the problems of ageing, and all nurses, if they are to understand new treatments, need a deeper knowledge of biology and physiology. Nursing has become more linked with the social sciences. Because of this, in the last few years a number of schools of nursing have developed joint courses with universities so that students can obtain a degree related to their course for registration. Apart from joint courses, the universities of Manchester and Wales now offer a Degree in Nursing.

59 The first candidates for the Bachelor of Nursing degree at the Welsh School of Medicine graduated in 1976. The University of Manchester also awards a degree in nursing and a number of hospitals have arrangements with universities so that selected candidates can do a joint nursing and degree course.

Compared with half a century ago, nurses now need a wider education and a number of different types of nurse are required. Some give basic care in the hospital and on the district; others perform complicated technical tasks and assist with surgery, where machines now look like the front panel of a jet plane; others specialize in one aspect of a particular branch of nursing such as coronary care or drug addiction. These new demands have led people to question whether the present arrangements for nurses' training are still suitable. Nurses themselves have been critical and have suggested a number of changes.

In 1970 the government, in response to promptings from the profession, set up its own Committee on Nursing Education under the chairmanship of Professor Asa Briggs. The report, which has been accepted, contains a number of exciting suggestions. A new system that would accommodate all candidates with the right aptitude and personality is advocated. The principle is not unlike that in comprehensive schools, where pupils concentrate on their own potential and progress at different rates. All students of nursing would go to 'Colleges of Nursing', but these would not be formal buildings so much as places within a given district where students would learn both theory and practice. Education and experience would go hand in hand and would be gained by a series of blocks or 'modules', which would include work in general and mental hospitals and on the district. The first group of five blocks would take 18 months and would be the foundation stone; when this was laid the student would be a Certified Nurse and able to practise under supervision. After the 'foundation' some students might give up and others leave for marriage, but some would carry on at College and build more blocks on the foundation. The next modules would be taken in greater depth, rather like Advanced Level certificates. This second course would enable students to become Registered Nurses. Now the student could take a higher education course and specialize in one branch of nursing, such as children's nursing or health visiting; some students would take diplomas in teaching, others would do courses in management. Once the foundation stone was laid the wall could be built in a variety of patterns with a number of different blocks to different levels. It may be some time before these suggestions can be fully implemented and when they are there may be variations on the theme. However, if nurses are to be prepared for an ever-changing world, a flexible but progressive system of education would seem more appropriate than the present method of collecting different certificates for proficiency in different branches of nursing from different bodies.

Nursing Service Today

The patients in acute hospitals are either very ill or in need of sophisticated treatment and drugs. This makes some forms of hospital nursing more 'intensive' and concentrated than others. Generally speaking, nurses on these units are specially trained and because of this they are able to cope with the strain of always dealing with very ill patients and their relatives. Moreover, nurses are now members of a large team which may include engineers, technicians, laboratory workers and physiotherapists as well as a variety of nursing and medical colleagues. Apart from the satisfaction gained when a seriously ill patient recovers, there is now a new satisfaction in being a member of a team and learning from the skills of others.

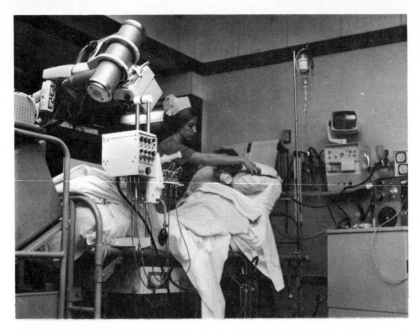

60 The patient is hooked up in the Intensive Care Unit. Controlling all these tubes, knobs and dials requires a sound knowledge of physiology. It is important that the nurse not only understands what is happening but also *why* it is happening.

61 A state-enrolled nurse helps an elderly patient. The enrolled nurse does a two-year training that concentrates on the practical aspects of nursing. There are now nearly 50,000 enrolled nurses working in all branches of nursing.

62 More and more nursing is being done in the community. This means that more district nurses are required and today they have to carry out a wide range of duties.

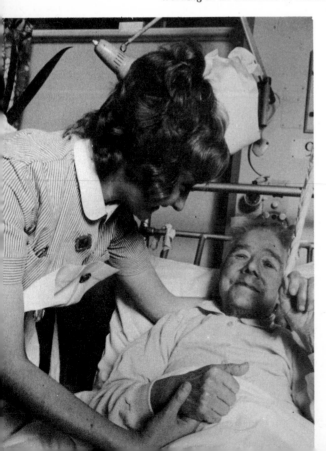

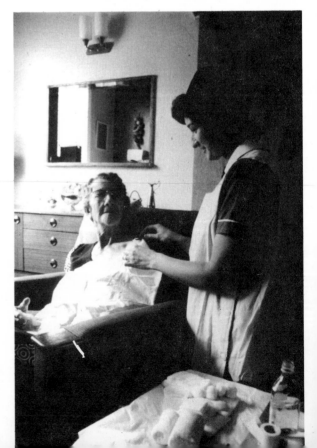

However, the acutely ill are but a small proportion of those in hospital. Far more patients, particularly the elderly, are being taught to live with handicaps, being rehabilitated and returned to independence. Instead of rows of apathetic people in bed, the ward is now a hive of activity. But if the nurse is to help the patient to live again, she herself must have knowledge and assurance together with a personality that inspires confidence. Again the nurse is a member of a team, co-operating with social workers, welfare officers and physiotherapists and maintaining close relations with colleagues in the community and the relatives to whom the patient will be returned.

Nowhere have changes been more marked than in the community. As we have seen, district nursing and health visiting grew up to meet the social needs of the nineteenth century, and until recently both worked from the Town or County Hall. However, even before the health services were reorganized, doctors and nurses in the community had worked out new ways of co-operation. In the past few years it has become common for district nurses and health visitors to be 'attached' to a group of family doctors. The doctors and nurses now form a team and work together to give care to the people in the practice.

Because of early discharges from hospital, to make more beds available, the district nurse is now often required to do 'acute' nursing. High hospital costs have promoted research into how hospital equipment can be converted into 'do it yourself' home kits, and machines that were once the wonder of hospitals are now found as standard portable equipment in the back of the district nurse's car. But often the district nurse will have to do treatment in cramped conditions without proper plumbing and, in an emergency, there is no bell to push or passing houseman to come to her aid. As Miss Nightingale said, 'The district nurse is on her own.'

63 The health visitor sets out on her visits. These will probably include visits to help and advise old people living alone, mothers with young babies and handicapped persons. A good deal of the health visitor's time is devoted to people with special social and medical problems.

Longer life, early marriage, working wives and the increase in the number of elderly living alone have changed the work of the health visitor. At the beginning of the century mothers, often poor and underfed, neglected their children because they were too weak to care. Today few people are underfed and most are above the poverty line. But now new problems appear. Firstly, when families are small there are fewer relatives to help in time of trouble, and those there are live far away or are out at work. Secondly, unlike Victorian families where a new baby appeared every year or so, children from small families grow up with little experience of babies. Thirdly, although some modern conveniences make life easier, other pressures make it more difficult. People expect both to do and have more, and this leads to conflict about the way time and money are spent. Some people resolve conflicts, others break down and, unable to cope, some parents even 'batter' their babies. Trying to detect and help such families is now a main task of the health visitor.

New Opportunities for Nurses

Today nurses help to plan and manage at all levels of the health service. These nurses 'administer' and help other nurses to work more efficiently. The Department of Health and Social Services has a Chief Nursing Officer and a team of assistants, who combine being nurses with being civil servants. A few nurses have become experts in planning hospitals and work with architects and planning teams; others have made a study of time and labour saving and have become 'work study' officers. As the Health Service is now one of the largest employers of labour, the nurses themselves need a number of supporting services. Some become personnel officers and look after their colleagues and deal with their many employment problems. Others specialize in the prevention of ill health among nursing staff and provide a Staff Health Service.

All nurses, as Miss Nightingale pointed out, must be educators, but with a growing variety of courses and more emphasis on ward and district teaching, more and more nurses are devoting much of their time to teaching others, and some of course must teach the teachers.

Apart from the variety of jobs for nurses in administration and teaching, there are new possibilities for nurses with patients. Some nurses, by experience and study, develop special skills in a particular and difficult type of nursing, such as the care of the dying or the nursing of patients in drug addiction units. These nurses are sometimes used as advisers to others, and as we become more research-minded about the best ways of giving care this is a development that is likely to continue.

Nursing outside the National Health Service

Although the National Health Service employs 140,000 trained nurses and 76,000 in training, there are a number of nurses working outside the services. Compared with years ago very few nurses work in private houses, although a number work in nursing homes. However, it is in industry and commerce that the scope for nursing has increased since the war. Employers are much more conscious of the value of health and safety and trade unions are more active in demanding it. Some large undertakings — such as Unilever, Imperial Chemicals Industries and British Steel — employ a full-scale medical service. Small undertakings, on the other hand, may employ only one nurse and perhaps a part-time doctor.

64 The main task of the occupational health nurse is to ensure that the work force remains healthy. Here she is watching the job being done and ensuring that safety measures are taken.

The main task of the nurse in industry is to know the hazards of the industry, to help prevent accidents and to ensure the work force is kept healthy. To do this successfully the nurse needs a special training in what is called Occupational Health. The life of the nurse in industry is varied and interesting. Part of her time will be devoted to going round the plant or place of work to observe risks and note whether people are protected. Another duty will be to conduct medical checks and ensure that people are fit and suited for the jobs they do; for example, has a precision worker the right eyesight? Although the main duties are the prevention of accidents and ill health, an industrial nurse is also responsible for running a surgery, dealing with accidents and ensuring that sick workers get the right attention and a check-up before they return to work. Each day will be different and many nurses find working in industry both challenging and stimulating.

65 Nurses decide for themselves: the Briggs Conference on Nursing Education, 1972. Today, nurses play an important part in planning the future of the nursing services.

In Chapter 7 we saw how nursing developed as an 'organized profession'. This meant that nurses did for themselves many things that had hitherto been done for them by other people. Previously doctors, civil servants and distinguished laymen decided what nurses should do, how they should be trained and how they should be paid. Now these decisions are made, at least in part, by nurses themselves. All these changes led to new opportunities for nurses with special aptitudes. Today there are nurse journalists, nurse editors, nurses who make a study of negotiation, nurses engaged in research. There are nurses in universities and nurses who are professors. Nursing offers scope to many different talents.

Although these developments seem a far call from Miss Nightingale and her 'superintendents', they all exist for the same reason: to enable the nurse at the bedside to give a better service.

We have traced nursing through many changes: from the vocation of nuns, through the attendants of the eighteenth century to the professional nurse of today. Now, because of changes in medicine, the wheel has gone full circle. Because they had little medical knowledge and could not cure, the nuns concentrated on 'care'. But they knew that care must be given to those 'afflicted in mind, body and estate' and that mental and physical health and welfare were often inseparable. In the intervening centuries medical science has developed so that many diseases are now prevented and those not prevented can often be cured. Today, apart from accidents, we mainly have to face illnesses that cannot be prevented or cured. What is left is care. The disabled, the old and the chronic sick have problems of 'mind, body and estate' that are interdependent. With this challenge, nursing returns from being an adjunct to cure to what the Briggs Committee called 'The Major Caring Profession'.

Further Reading

J.J. Bagley, *Life in Medieval England* (Batsford, 1965)

M. Bruce, *The Coming of the Welfare State* (Batsford, 1968)

D. Courtney, *The Story of England's Hospitals* (Museum Press, 1961)

D. Edwardes-Rees, *The Story of Nursing* (Constable, 1965)

N. Grant, *The Industrial Revolution* (Watts, 1973)

J. Harris, *The Welfare State* (Batsford, 1973)

S. & V. Leff, *From Witchcraft to World Health* (Lawrence and Wishart, 1956)

I. Martin, *From Workhouse to Welfare State* (Penguin, 1970)

F. Nightingale, *Notes on Nursing 1859* (Duckworth, 1952)

M. Purcell, *The World of Monsieur Vincent* (Harvill Press, 1963)

L. Rose, *Health and Hygiene* (Batsford, 1975)

C. Woodham Smith, *Miss Florence Nightingale* (Constable, 1950)

H. Zinner, *Rats, Lice and History* (Bantam Books, 1960)

Index

The numbers in **bold** type refer to the figure numbers of the illustrations

North East and Cumbria NHS Libraries

NEC00001727

WX
41
BAL

610.73

East Cumbria School of Nursing

EAST CUMBRIA
SCHOOL OF NURSING